PRENTICE HALL MATHEMATICS

COURSE 1

Guided Problem Solving Masters

PEARSON

Prentice
Hall

Needham, Massachusetts
Upper Saddle River, New Jersey

ISBN: 0-13-037798-8

1 2 3 4 5 6 7 8 9 10   07 06 05 04 03

Guided Problem Solving Masters

Contents

Contents (continued)

To The Teacher

Overview

Guided Problem Solving Masters provide a step-by-step approach to solve a problem selected from the Prentice Hall Mathematics *Course 1–3* student books. Some of these selections are routine in nature and cover basic concepts. Others are nonroutine and might involve multiple-step problems, problems with too much information, problems involving critical thinking, and so on. An icon in the Teacher's Edition flags the selected problem so that the teacher will know what problem is provided on the master.

How to use

The *Guided Problem Solving Masters* are designed so that the teacher can use them in many different ways.

a. As a teaching tool to guide students in exploring and mastering a specific problem-solving skill or strategy. Making a transparency of the worksheet provides an excellent way to expedite this process as students work along with the teacher at their desks.

b. As additional practice in solving problems for students who have had difficulty in completing the assignment.

c. As independent or group work to help students reach a better understanding of the problem-solving process.

d. As a homework assignment that may encourage students to involve their parents in the educational process.

Description of the master

Each master gives the page and exercise number of the problem upon which it is based. That problem is stated at the top of each master. The master is divided into the three steps of the problem-solving process that is used throughout the student text. Each step includes key questions designed to guide students through the problem-solving process. At the bottom of the master, *Solve Another Problem* allows students to use their skills to solve a problem similar to the original problem. This helps reinforce the problem-solving skills and strategies they have just used in solving the problem on the master.

The Guided Problem Solving template on the next page can be used to help students organize their work as they complete the *Solve Another Problem*. It may also be used to assist students in solving any problem as they complete the three steps of the problem-solving process.

GPS Guided Problem Solving

Read and Understand

Plan and Solve

Look Back and Check

1-1 • Guided Problem Solving

GPS **Student Page 7, Exercise 27:**

Apples Order the apple types from least to greatest number of cartons.

Type of Apple	Cartons
Idared	2,753,000
Empire	2,739,000
Braeburn	2,198,000
McIntosh	3,304,000
York	3,212,000

Read and Understand

1. Where is the information you need to do the exercise?

   _____

2. How do you determine which number is the least?

   _____

   _____

Plan and Solve

3. Which apple type has the least number of cartons? _____

4. Which apple type has the most number of cartons? _____

5. Which apple type has the second most number of cartons? _____

6. Which apple type has the second least number of cartons? _____

7. Order the apple types from least to greatest by name.

   _____

8. Order the apple types from least to greatest by number of cartons.

   _____

Look Back and Check

9. Explain another way to do this problem.

   _____

   _____

Solve Another Problem

10. Order the populations from least to greatest, by city.

Philadephia	New York City	Chicago	Los Angeles	San Francisco
5,899,345	18,087,251	8,065,633	14,531,529	6,253,311

_____

_____

1-2 • Guided Problem Solving

GPS Student Page 11, Exercise 39:

Heights Artists use a ratio called the Golden Mean to describe a person's height. Your height from the floor to your waist is usually six hundred eighteen thousandths of your total height. Write this number as a decimal.

Read and Understand

1. Is the number more or less than 1? Explain.

   _____

   _____

2. The word *thousandths* represents how many decimal places to the right of the decimal point?

   _____

Plan and Solve

3. Write the whole number part and the decimal. _____

4. Which place does the 8 go? _____

5. Which place does 1 go? _____

6. Which place does 6 go? _____

7. Fill in the three decimal places to the right of the decimal place.

   _____

Look Back and Check

8. Why do you think your answer to Exercise 7 is correct?

   _____

   _____

Solve Another Problem

9. Liz needs to write to the company that made her entertainment center because she is missing a bolt needed to put it together. The bolt she needs measures 1.03 cm. How should Liz write this number in words?

   _____

1-3 • Guided Problem Solving

GPS **Student Page 16, Exercise 20:**

Population About 11.02 million people live in Jakarta, Indonesia. About 11.7 million people live in Delhi, India. About 11.79 million people live in Karachi, Pakistan. Order these cities from least to greatest population.

Read and Understand

1. How many cities are discussed in the problem? _____

2. What are you asked to do?

   _____

3. Circle the populations that you need to order.

Plan and Solve

4. Use placeholders to write the three numbers with the same number of decimal places

   _____

5. Which number is the smallest?

   _____

6. Which number is the largest?

   _____

7. Write the numbers in order from least to greatest.

   _____

8. Order the cities from least to greatest population.

   _____

Look Back and Check

9. Do the smallest and middle populations have smaller decimal values than the largest number?

   _____

Solve Another Problem

10. Jessie ran 3 miles in 20.53 minutes. Anne ran the same distance in 20.02 minutes. Kara ran the same distance in 20.96 minutes. Order the runners from fastest to slowest.

   _____

1-4 • Guided Problem Solving

GPS **Student Page 21, Exercise 20:**

Packaging A ball has a mass of 283.5 grams. You want to ship 9 balls in a box. The box has a mass of 595.34 grams. Estimate the total mass.

Read and Understand

1. Circle the information you will need to solve.

2. What are you being asked to do?

   _____

3. Does it tell you what place to round to? If not, what place do you plan to round to?

   _____

Plan and Solve

4. What is the mass of a ball to the nearest hundred grams?

   _____

5. What is the mass of nine balls?

   _____

6. What is the mass of the box to the nearest hundred grams?

   _____

7. Write an expression that can be used to solve the problem.

   _____

8. Estimate the total mass.

   _____

Look Back and Check

9. What units should your answer have?

   _____

Solve Another Problem

10. A textbook has a mass of 2,267.96 grams. You want to ship 5 textbooks in a box. The box has a mass of 606.23 grams. Estimate the total mass to the nearest thousand.

    _____

1-5 • Guided Problem Solving

GPS **Student Page 28, Exercise 24:**

Population In the 2000 Census, the New England states had a total population of about 13.92 million. Find the population of Maine.

State	Population
Connecticut	3.41 million
Maine	?
Massachusetts	6.35 million
New Hampshire	1.24 million
Rhode Island	1.05 million
Vermont	0.61 million

Read and Understand

1. What are you being asked to do?

   _____

2. How will you use the total population of the New England states to answer the question?

   _____

Plan and Solve

3. Find the sum of the populations of the other states.

   _____

4. What is the total population of all the New England states?

   _____

5. Write an expression to find the population of Maine.

   _____

6. Evaluate the expression to find the population of Maine.

   _____

7. Find the population of Maine.

   _____

Look Back and Check

8. How can you check your answer?

   _____

   _____

Solve Another Problem

9. You and a friend calculate your grade for a class. You have an 83.5% and your friend has an 85.65%. Who has the higher grade? How much higher is it?

   _____

   _____

1-6 • Guided Problem Solving

GPS Student Page 32, Exercise 5:

It takes Clara 12 minutes to cut a log into 4 pieces. How long will it take her to cut another log that is the same size into 5 pieces?

Read and Understand

1. What are you being asked to do?

   _____

   _____

2. List the information you need to answer the question.

   _____

   _____

3. Do you expect for it to take her longer or shorter than 12 minutes? Explain.

   _____

   _____

Plan and Solve

4. How long does it take her to cut 4 pieces?

   _____

5. How long does it take her to cut 1 piece?

   _____

6. How long will it take her to cut 5 pieces?

   _____

Look Back and Check

7. Why does it take her 3 minutes longer to cut 5 pieces?

   _____

   _____

Solve Another Problem

8 . You can read 20 pages in 15 minutes. How many minutes will it take you to read 152 pages of the same book?

   _____

1-7 • Guided Problem Solving

GPS **Student Page 38, Exercise 44:**

Nutrition There is 0.2 gram of calcium in 1 serving of cheddar cheese. How much calcium is in 3.25 servings of cheddar cheese?

Read and Understand

1. What is being compared in the exercise?

    _____

    _____

2. What are you being asked to do?

    _____

3. Will you multiply or divide to determine the answer? Explain.

    _____

    _____

Plan and Solve

4. How much calcium is in one serving? _____

5. How many servings do you want?

    _____

6. Write an expression to answer the exercise.

    _____

7. How many grams of calcium are in 3.25 servings of cheddar cheese?

    _____

Look Back and Check

8. Should there be more or less than 0.2 gram of calcium in 3.25 servings of cheddar cheese? Explain.

    _____

Solve Another Problem

9. There are 0.5 gram of fat in one serving of a breakfast cereal. How many grams of fat are in 4.25 servings?

    _____

1-8 • Guided Problem Solving

GPS **Student Page 41, Exercise 17:**

Dolphins Dolphins swim about 27.5 miles per hour. A person can swim about 0.1 times as fast as a dolphin. How fast can a person swim?

Read and Understand

1. What is the problem comparing?

   _____

2. What are you being asked to do?

   _____

3. Which swims faster a person or a dolphin? Explain.

   _____

   _____

Plan and Solve

4. How fast do dolphins swim? _____

5. How fast does a person swim
   compared to a dolphin? _____

6. Do you multiply or divide by 0.1
   to determine the answer? _____

7. How many places do you move
   the decimal point? _____

8. Do you move the decimal
   to the left or to the right? _____

9 How fast can a person swim? _____

Look Back and Check

10. Is the speed of a person you determined
    less than or greater than the speed of a dolphin? _____

Solve Another Problem

11. A person can run about 0.1 times as fast as a cheetah. If a cheetah runs an average of 60 miles per hour, how fast can a person run?

    _____

1-9 • Guided Problem Solving

GPS Student Page 46, Exercise 38:

School Supplies A stack of paper measures 0.9 centimeter thick.
Each piece of paper is 0.01 centimeter thick.

a. How many pieces of paper are in the stack?

b. Could each of 25 students get three pieces of paper?

Read and Understand

1. Circle the information you will need to solve.

2. What are you being asked to do in part *a*?

   _____

3. What are you being asked to do in part *b*?

   _____

   _____

Plan and Solve

4. How thick is one piece of paper? _____

5. How thick is the stack of paper? _____

6. Do you multiply or divide to answer part a? _____

7. Write an expression to answer part a. _____

8. How many pieces of paper are in the stack? _____

9. How many pieces of paper are needed for each of 25 students to
   get three pieces of paper?

   _____

10. Is there enough paper? _____

Look Back and Check

11. Why is the number of pieces of paper 100 times more than the
    height of the stack of paper?

    _____

Solve Another Problem

12. A stack of baseball cards measures 5.4 centimeter thick. Each
    baseball card is 0.1 centimeter thick. How many baseball cards
    are in the stack?

    _____

1-10 • Guided Problem Solving

GPS **Student Page 50, Exercise 28:**

Coins There are 312 coins of the same type in two stacks. One stack of coins is 15 inches tall. The other stack is 9 inches tall. Find the thickness of one coin to the nearest thousandth of an inch.

Read and Understand

1. List the information you need to solve the problem.

   _____

   _____

2. What are you being asked to do?

   _____

   _____

Plan and Solve

3. How tall are the two stacks combined? _____

4. How tall are 312 coins? _____

5. How can you determine the thickness of one coin?

   _____

6. How thick is one coin?

   _____

Look Back and Check

7. Multiply the thickness you determined in Exercise 6 by 312.
   Does this answer match the total thickness of all 312 coins?

   _____

   _____

Solve Another Problem

8. There are 500 compact discs of the same type in two stacks. One stack is 7 inches tall. The other stack is 13 inches tall. Find the thickness of one compact disc to the nearest hundredth of an inch.

   _____

2-1 • Guided Problem Solving

GPS Student Page 66, Exercise 26:

Business A dry cleaner charges $5.00 to clean one item. He offers to clean a second item for $4.50, and a third item for $4.00.

a. If he continues to subtract $.50 for each additional item, how much will it cost to clean six items?

b. If the pattern continues, which item will be cleaned for free?

Read and Understand

1. What are you being asked to do in part *a*?

   _____

2. What are you being asked to do in part *b*?

   _____

3. What problem solving strategy will best solve this problem?

   _____

Plan and Solve

4. What is the cost of the 4th item? _____

5. What is the cost of the 5th item? _____

6. What is the cost of the 6th item? _____

7. Write and evaluate an expression for the cost of six items.

   _____

8. What is the cost of the 7th, 8th, 9th, and 10th items?

   _____

9. Which item will be cleaned for free? _____

Look Back and Check

10. Can you think of another way to solve the problem? Explain.

    _____

Solve Another Problem

11. Susie is trying to increase the distance she runs. The first week she ran $\frac{1}{2}$ mi, the second week she ran $\frac{3}{4}$ mi, the third week she ran 1 mile. How far will she run during the sixth week?

    _____

2-2 • Guided Problem Solving

GPS Student Page 71, Exercise 30:

Bricklayer's Formula The formula $N = 7 \times \ell \times h$ gives the number of bricks needed for a wall of length ℓ feet and height h feet. How many bricks are needed for a wall with length 22 feet and height 30 feet?

Read and Understand

1. What are you being asked to do?

   _____

   _____

2. What does N represent?

   _____

Plan and Solve

3. What is the formula for the number of bricks?

   _____

4. What do you replace ℓ and w with? _____

5. Replace ℓ and w with the values. _____

6. Simplify the expression. _____

7. How many bricks are needed? _____

Look Back and Check

8. How can you check your answer? Use your method to see if your answer is correct.

   _____

   _____

   _____

Solve Another Problem

9. The sum of the interior angles of a polygon can be found using the formula $S = (N - 2) \times 180°$, where N is the number of sides of the polygon. What is the sum of the interior angles of a polygon with 8 sides?

   _____

2-3 • Guided Problem Solving

GPS **Student Page 77, Exercise 22:**

Zoo On Saturday, admission to the zoo costs $3 per person. The Sengs have a coupon for a discount of $5 off for a family. There are p people in the Seng family. Write an expression for how much the Sengs pay for admission to the zoo if they use the coupon.

Read and Understand

1. What are you being asked to do?

   _____

   _____

   _____

2. What does the variable represent in the expression?

   _____

3. Circle the information you will need to solve the problem.

Plan and Solve

4. How much does admission to the zoo cost for each person?

   _____

5. Write an expression for the cost of the tickets if there are p people in the Seng family.

   _____

6. Write an expression for the cost of the tickets if there are p people in the Seng family and they use the $5 coupon.

   _____

Look Back and Check

7. Could you write the expression another way? Explain.

   _____

Solve Another Problem

8. Each room in Anna's house needs 4 outlet covers. Write an expression that describes the total number of outlet covers Anna bought if she still needs 2 outlet covers.

   _____

2-4 • Guided Problem Solving

GPS **Student Page 81, Exercise 7:**

Band Tia, Lewis, and Jill play trombone. Wendi, Pali, and Nigel play baritone. How many different pairs of a trombone player and a baritone player are there?

Read and Understand

1. What are you being asked to do?

   _____

2. What problem solving strategy will best solve this problem?

   _____

Plan and Solve

3. If Tia is the trombone player, how many pairs are possible?

   _____

4. If Lewis is the trombone player, how many pairs are possible?

   _____

5. If Jill is the trombone player, how many pairs are possible?

   _____

6. How do you find the total pairs possible?

   _____

7. How many total pairs are there? _____

Look Back and Check

8. What other strategy could you use to solve this problem? Do you get same answer?

   _____

Solve Another Problem

9. This year Leo can choose three of his classes. For his language he can choose Spanish, French, or Latin. For his art class he can choose drawing, ceramics, or photo shop. For his science he can choose either physical science or chemistry. How many different cominations are there for Leo's schedule?

   _____

2-5 • Guided Problem Solving

GPS Student Page 87, Exercise 29:

Pollution When burned, 18 gallons of gasoline produce about 360 pounds of carbon dioxide. Solve the equation $18n = 360$ to find how much carbon dioxide 1 gallon produces.

Read and Understand

1. What are you being asked to do?

   _____

   _____

2. How can mental math help you to solve this problem?

   _____

   _____

Plan and Solve

3. What does the equation, $18n = 360$, mean?

   _____

4. What is $360 \div 18$? _____

5. How many times more carbon dioxide is produced compared to the amount of gasoline?

   _____

6. For 1 gallon of gasoline, how much carbon dioxide is produced?

   _____

Look Back and Check

7. Why is the amount of carbon dioxide 20 times more than the amount of gasoline?

   _____

   _____

Solve Another Problem

8. At a school, there are 72 teachers for 1,872 students. If all the teachers have the same amount of students, use the equation, $72n = 1,872$ to find how many students 1 teacher has.

   _____

2-6 • Guided Problem Solving

GPS Student Page 93, Exercise 30:

You buy a poster and a framing kit. The total cost is $18.95. You have
$7.05 left in your wallet. Write and solve an equation to find
how much money was in your wallet before these purchases.

Read and Understand

1. What are you being asked to do?

   _____

   _____

2. What will the variable represent in the equation?

   _____

   _____

3. Circle the information you will need to solve.

Plan and Solve

4. How much did you pay for the poster and framing kit? _____

5. Write an expression for the amount in your wallet minus
   the amount you paid for the poster and the framing kit.
   Choose any variable for the amount in your wallet. _____

6. How much money was left in your wallet
   after the purchase?

   _____

7. Write an equation comparing the amounts
   in Steps 5 and 6.

   _____

8. What do you do to both sides of the
   equation to isolate the variable?

   _____

9. Solve the equation.

   _____

10. How much money was in your
    wallet before the purchases? _____

Look Back and Check

11. Explain how you can check your answer. Then check your
    answer. _____

Solve Another Problem

12. Jim has saved $78. This is $23 more than his sister has saved. Write
    and solve an equation to find how much has his sister has saved?

    _____

2-7 • Guided Problem Solving

GPS **Student Page 97, Exercise 30:**

Biology An adult female elephant's height is about 5.5 times the length of her hind footprint. Use an equation to find the approximate height of an adult female elephant whose hind footprint is 1.5 feet long.

Read and Understand

1. What are you being asked to do?

   _____

   _____

   _____

2. Circle the information you will need to solve.

3. The word set *5.5 times* tells you to perform what operation?

   _____

Plan and Solve

4. What is the length of the hind footprint of this particular adult female elephant? _____

5. Write an expression to represent the phrase, *5.5 times the length of the hind footprint.* _____

6. Write an equation for the height of the elephant. _____

7. What is the height of the elephant? _____

Look Back and Check

8. Explain how you can check your answer. Does your answer check?

   _____

   _____

Solve Another Problem

9. Angela makes 1.75 times the amount of money that Janet makes. If Janet makes $38,200, how much does Angela make? Write and solve an equation.

   _____

2-8 • Guided Problem Solving

GPS Student Page 102, Exercise 40:

Biology Suppose a single-celled animal splits in two after one hour. Each new cell also splits in two after one hour. How many cells will there be after eight hours? Write your answer using an exponent.

Read and Understand

1. What are you being asked to do?

_____

_____

2. Explain what it means to write a number with an exponent.

_____

_____

_____

Plan and Solve

3. How many cells are there after 3 hours?
   Write the number using an exponent. _____

4. How many cells are there after 4 hours?
   Write the number using an exponent. _____

5. How many cells are there after 6 hours?
   Write the number using an exponent. _____

6. How many cells are there after 8 hours?
   Write the number using an exponent. _____

Look Back and Check

7. Why is the exponent 8?

_____

Solve Another Problem

8. An organism divides into 3 different organisms after the first hour. Each of those 3 organisms divide into 3 different organisms after the second hour. If this pattern continues, how many organisms are there after 4 hours? Write the number using an exponent.

_____

2-9 • Guided Problem Solving

GPS Student Page 107, Exercise 16:

Gardening Your school's ecology club plants 8 rows of sunflowers in a vacant lot. Each row has 27 plants. Find the total number of sunflowers that the ecology club plants.

Read and Understand

1. What are you being asked to do?

   _____

2. Circle the information you will need to solve.

Plan and Solve

3. How many rows of sunflowers are there?

   _____

4. How many sunflowers are there in each row?

   _____

5. Write an expression for the total number of sunflowers.

   _____

6. Simplify the expression.

   _____

7. How many sunflowers are there total?

   _____

Look Back and Check

8. Explain how you check your answer. Does your answer check?

   _____

   _____

Solve Another Problem

9. Alyce is tiling her living room. She tiles one row with blue tiles and the next row with white tiles. There are 15 blue rows and 14 white rows. There are 8 tiles in each row. How many tiles are there total?

   _____

3-1 • Guided Problem Solving

GPS **Student Page 122, Exercise 40:**

Money Elissa and eight friends have lunch at a restaurant. The bill is $56.61. Can the group split the bill into nine equal shares? Use the rule for divisibility by 9 to explain your answer.

Read and Understand

1. What are you being asked to do?

_____

_____

2. What do you have to use to explain your answer?

_____

3. What is the divisibility rule for 9?

_____

_____

Plan and Solve

4. How much is the bill? _____

5. What are the digits? _____

6. What is the sum of the digits? _____

7. Does 9 divide evenly into the sum? _____

8. Can the group split the bill into nine equal shares?_____

Look Back and Check

9. How can you check that your answer is correct?

_____

_____

Solve Another Problem

10. Melissa, Dyanna, and Cristina are counselors at a summer camp. They want to divide the campers evenly among them. If there are 137 campers, use the rule for divisibility by 3 to detemine if this is possible.

_____

3-2 • Guided Problem Solving

GPS Student Page 125, Exercise 27:

Parades A group has 36 ceremonial guards. When they march, they form rows of equal numbers of guards. What numbers of rows can they make? How many guards will be in each row?

Read and Understand

1. What are you being asked to do?

_____

_____

2. What do you have to know to do this problem?

_____

3. How many answers are there to this question?

_____

Plan and Solve

4. List the factors of 36.

_____

5. What are the possible row lengths?

_____

6. For each row length, how many people are in each row?

_____

Look Back and Check

7. How can you check your answer?

_____

_____

Solve Another Problem

8. Louise is planting 18 bunches of pansies in her garden. She wants to put them in rows of equal plants. What numbers of rows can they make? How many pansies will be in each row?

_____

3-3 • Guided Problem Solving

GPS Student Page 130, Exercise 27:

Baseball Cards Three friends pool their money to buy baseball cards. Brand A has 8 cards in each pack, Brand B has 12 cards, and Brand C has 15 cards. If they want to split the cards equally, which two brands should they buy? Explain.

Read and Understand

1. What does *split the cards equally* mean?

   _____

Plan and Solve

2. How many cards will they have if they buy Brand A and Brand B?

   _____

3. Is the number you found in Exercise 3, divisible by 3? Why or why not?

   _____

4. How many cards will they have if they buy Brand A and Brand C?

   _____

5. How many cards will they have if they buy Brand B and Brand C?

   _____

6. Which of the answers to Exercises 4 and 5 are divisible by 3? _____

7. Which two brands should they buy?

   _____

Look Back and Check

8. Explain your decision.

   _____

Solve Another Problem

9. Carrie is lining up 45 students in the drill team and 25 students in the color guard. She wants each row to have the same number of students in both groups. How many rows are there, and how many students are in each row?

   _____

   _____

3-4 • Guided Problem Solving

GPS **Student Page 136, Exercise 31:**

Traffic Planning Two traffic engineers are writing about the average driving time between two towns. One engineer writes the time as 45, but the other writes it as $\frac{3}{4}$. What could explain the difference?

Read and Understand

1. What are you being asked to do?

    _____

    _____

2. What is the relationship between the two measurements?

    _____

Plan and Solve

3. Name some units in which time can be measured.

    _____

    _____

4. What is a reasonable unit for the engineer who wrote 45?

    _____

5. What is a reasonable unit for the engineer who wrote $\frac{3}{4}$?

    _____

6. What explains the difference?

    _____

    _____

Look Back and Check

7. Why did you choose those units?

    _____

    _____

Solve Another Problem

8. A scientist measured the time it took for a reaction to take place as $\frac{1}{4}$ hour. To use the results, he needs to write the numbers as minutes. How many minutes did it take for the reaction to take place?

    _____

3-5 • Guided Problem Solving

GPS Student Page 141, Exercise 37:

Food A caterer plans to serve two slices of melon to each of 50 guests. She estimates getting 12 slices from each melon. Write the number of melons she will use as a mixed number. How many whole melons does she need?

Read and Understand

1. Circle the information you will need to solve.

2. What are you being asked to do?

   _____

   _____

Plan and Solve

3. How many slices does she need to feed 50 guests?

   _____

4. How many slices does she get from each melon?

   _____

5. What operation do you use to find the number of melons she needs?

   _____

6. Write the number of melons she will use as a mixed number.

   _____

7. How many *whole* melons does she need?

   _____

Look Back and Check

8. Why does she need to know how many whole melons are needed?

   _____

Solve Another Problem

9. Three hundred twenty-one students are going on a field trip. One bus can seat 48 students. Write the number of buses needed as a mixed number. How many whole buses are needed?

   _____

3-6 • Guided Problem Solving

GPS **Student Page 145, Exercise 17:**

Business During a promotion, a music store gives a free CD to every fifteenth customer and a free DVD to every fortieth customer. Which customer will be the first to get both a free CD and a free DVD?

Read and Understand

1. Circle the information you will need to solve.

2. What are you being asked to do?

   _____

   _____

Plan and Solve

3. Which customers will receive a free CD?

   _____

   _____

4. Which customers will receive a free DVD?

   _____

5. Which customer will be the first to get both a free CD and a free DVD?

   _____

Look Back and Check

6. Explain how you can check your answer.

   _____

Solve Another Problem

7. Emanuel, Michelle, and Kim volunteer at the swimming pool. Emanuel works every 5 days. Michelle works every 6 days. Kim works every 15 days. They are working together today. How many days will it be until the next time they work together?

   _____

   _____

   _____

   _____

3-7 • Guided Problem Solving

GPS **Student Page 151, Exercise 23:**

Shopping Two sports drinks have the same price. The cherry-flavored drink is $12\frac{9}{20}$ ounces. The blueberry-flavored drink is $12\frac{7}{16}$ ounces. Assuming you like both flavors, which drink is the better buy?

Read and Understand

1. Circle the information you will need to solve.

2. What are you being asked to do?

   _____

3. Since both drinks are priced the same, what do you have to determine?

   _____

Plan and Solve

4. What is the common denominator for
   $12\frac{9}{20}$ and $12\frac{7}{16}$? _____

5. Rewrite the fractional part of each mixed
   number with the common denominator. _____

6. Which fraction is bigger? _____

7. Which drink is the better buy? _____

Look Back and Check

8. What is another way you could answer this question?

   _____

   _____

Solve Another Problem

9. Mary, Ana, and Tim shared the driving on a trip. Mary drove $\frac{1}{8}$ of the distance. Ana drove $\frac{1}{4}$ of the distance. Did Mary or Ana drive more miles? Explain how you know.

   _____

3-8 • Guided Problem Solving

GPS Student Page 155, Exercise 25:

Shopping You order $1\frac{1}{4}$ pounds of cheese at a deli. What decimal number should the digital scale show?

Read and Understand

1. What are you being asked to do?

   _____

2. How do you read $\frac{1}{4}$ as a division problem?

   _____

Plan and Solve

3. How do you write 1 as a decimal?

   _____

4. Divide 1 by 4.

   _____

5. Write $1\frac{1}{4}$ as a decimal.

   _____

6. What decimal number should the digital scale show?

   _____

Look Back and Check

7. How can you check your answer?

   _____

Solve Another Problem

8. A recipe calls for $3\frac{3}{4}$ pounds of flour. Your scale only measures in decimals. What will the scale read?

   _____

3-9 • Guided Problem Solving

GPS **Student Page 159, Exercise 7:**

Trains leave Farmville for Lexinburg every 40 minutes. The first train leaves at 5:00 A.M. What is the departure time closest to 12:35 P.M.?

Read and Understand

1. Circle the information you will need to solve.

2. What are you being asked to do?

   _____

Plan and Solve

3. List the first 8 departure times.

   _____

4. What is the pattern?

   _____

   _____

   _____

   _____

5. Is 12:00 P.M. an even or odd hour? _____

6. How many departure times are there from
   12:00 P.M. – 1:00 P.M.? _____

7. What are the departure times? _____

8 What is the departure time closest to 12:35 P.M.? _____

Look Back and Check

9. Explain another method to answer this question.

   _____

Solve Another Problem

10. Buses leave for Downtown every 15 minutes. The first bus leaves at 7:15 A.M. What is the departure time closest to 10:25 A.M.?

    _____

    _____

4-1 • Guided Problem Solving

GPS **Student Page 173, Exercise 23:**

Coins Use the table at the right to estimate the total width of the coins shown in the picture.

U.S. Coins	
Coin	Diameter (inches)
Dime	$\frac{11}{16}$
Penny	$\frac{3}{4}$
Nickel	$\frac{13}{16}$
Quarter	$\frac{15}{16}$

Read and Understand

1. What are you being asked to do?

   _____

2. How are you supposed to use the table?

   _____

Plan and Solve

3. What is the actual width of the dime? _____

4. Is this fraction closer to $0, \frac{1}{2}$, or 1? _____

5. What are the actual widths of the dime, nickel, penny, and quarter?

   _____

6. Is the nickel's width closer to $0, \frac{1}{2}$, or 1? _____

7. Is the penny's width closer to $0, \frac{1}{2}$, or 1? _____

8. Is the quarter's width closer to $0, \frac{1}{2}$, or 1? _____

9. Estimate the total width of the coins. _____

Look Back and Check

10. Do you expect that your estimate is more or less than the actual length? Explain.

    _____

Solve Another Problem

11. The table shows the average precipitation for four months. Estimate the total amount of precipitation.

January	February	March	April
$3\frac{2}{3}$ in.	$1\frac{4}{7}$ in.	$2\frac{7}{8}$ in.	$4\frac{1}{2}$ in.

_____

4-2 • Guided Problem Solving

GPS **Student Page 177, Exercise 21:**

Biology Plasma makes up $\frac{11}{20}$ of your blood. Blood cells make up the other $\frac{9}{20}$. How much more of your blood is plasma than blood cells?

Read and Understand

1. What are you being asked to do?

   _____

2. What operation do you have use to answer this question?

   _____

Plan and Solve

3. How much of your blood is plasma?

   _____

4. How much of your blood is blood cells?

   _____

5. Write an expression you can use to answer the question.

   _____

6. How much more of your blood is plasma than blood cells?

   _____

Look Back and Check

7. How can you check your answer?

   _____

   _____

Solve Another Problem

8. Maddie has a window that is $15\frac{3}{8}$ inches long. She bought blinds that are $16\frac{5}{8}$ inches. How much longer are the blinds than the window?

   _____

4-3 • Guided Problem Solving

GPS **Student Page 183, Exercise 25:**

Weather A weather reporter records the rainfall as $\frac{3}{10}$ inch between 9:00 and 10:00 and $\frac{7}{8}$ inch between 10:00 and 11:00.

  a. **Estimation** Estimate the total rainfall between 9:00 and 11:00.

  b. What is the total rainfall between 9:00 and 11:00?

Read and Understand

1. What is the difference between part *a* and part *b*?

   _____

   _____

Plan and Solve

2. Estimate $\frac{3}{10}$ and $\frac{7}{8}$ separately. _____

3. Use the answers to Step 3 to estimate
   the total rainfall between 9:00 and 11:00. _____

4. What do you need to find the sum of the two measurements?

   _____

5. What is the least common denominator for $\frac{3}{10}$ and $\frac{7}{8}$? _____

6. Rewrite each fraction using the answer to Step 6. _____

7. What is the total rainfall between 9:00 and 11:00?

   _____

Look Back and Check

8. Does your answer match your estimate? Explain.

   _____

Solve Another Problem

9. A recipe for party mix calls for $\frac{3}{4}$ cup of cereal, $\frac{1}{4}$ cup of walnuts, $\frac{5}{8}$ cup of crackers, and $\frac{1}{2}$ cup of raisins. Estimate the number of cups in the mix. Determine the actual number of cups in the mix.

   _____

4-4 • Guided Problem Solving

Student Page 188, Exercise 18a:

Tides At low tide, the water is $4\frac{11}{12}$ feet deep. At high tide, the water depth increases by $2\frac{3}{4}$ feet. How deep is the water at high tide?

Read and Understand

1. Circle the information you will need to solve.

2. What operation do you need to answer the question?

_____

Plan and Solve

3. What is the least common denominator for $4\frac{11}{12}$ feet and $2\frac{3}{4}$ feet?

_____

4. Rewrite both fractions using the least common denominator.

_____

5. Write an expression you can use to answer the question.

_____

6. How deep is the water at high tide?

_____

Look Back and Check

7. How can you check your answer?

_____

_____

Solve Another Problem

8. Suppose Don will need to leave his fishing spot when the river reaches 30 feet. The river is predicted to rise $5\frac{7}{12}$ feet from its present level of $21\frac{7}{10}$ feet. Will he need to leave?

_____

_____

4-5 • Guided Problem Solving

GPS **Student Page 193, Exercise 28:**

On Monday, the snowfall in the mountains was $15\frac{3}{4}$ inches. On Tuesday, the snowfall was $18\frac{1}{2}$ inches. What was the difference in snowfall?

Read and Understand

1. Circle the information you will need to solve.

2. What are you being asked to do?

   _____

   _____

Plan and Solve

3. How many inches fell on Monday?

   _____

4. How many inches fell on Tuesday?

   _____

5. What common denominator do you need to use?

   _____

6. Rewrite each fraction using the least common denominator.

   _____

7. What was the difference in snowfall?

Look Back and Check

8. How can you check your answer?

   _____

Solve Another Problem

9. The perimeter of the lid to a rectangular box is $\frac{14}{6}$ yards. If the longer sides are $\frac{5}{6}$ yard, how long are the shorter sides? Explain.

   _____

4-6 • Guided Problem Solving

GPS Student Page 198, Exercise 22:

Landscaping The Service Club bought a 10-yard roll of edging to put around two trees in front of the school. They use $5\frac{2}{3}$ yards of edging for one tree and $3\frac{3}{4}$ yards for the other tree. How much edging is left?

Read and Understand

1. Circle the information you will need to solve.

2. How do you plan to solve this problem?

   _____

   _____

Plan and Solve

3. How much of the edging has been used?

   _____

4. Add these amounts together using a common denominator.

   _____

5. How much edging did the club purchase?

   _____

6. How much edging is left over?

   _____

Look Back and Check

7. Explain how you can check your answer.

   _____

Solve Another Problem

8. Linda bought a 15-yard roll of fabric to make a dress. She used $8\frac{1}{3}$ yards of fabric for the blouse and $5\frac{1}{4}$ yards for the pants. How much fabric is left?

   _____

4-7 • Guided Problem Solving

GPS Student Page 204, Exercise 22:

Clowns A clown wants to perform a 45-minute show at each of three birthday parties on the same Saturday. The first party must begin at 10:00 A.M. and he needs to leave the third party by 2:15 P.M. He wants to allow one hour between each party. Make a schedule for the clown.

Read and Understand

1. Circle the information you will need to solve.

2. What are you being asked to do?

   _____

3. What problem-solving method can you use to help create the schedule?

   _____

Plan and Solve

4. If the clown starts the first show at 10:00 A.M. when will he finish?

   _____

5. If he allows an hour between each show, when will the next show begin?

   _____

6. When will he finish the second show? _____

7. If he allows an hour between each show, when will the next show begin?

   _____

8. When will he finish the third show? _____

Look Back and Check

9. Did the clown finish when he was supposed to? _____

Solve Another Problem

10. If the clown's schedule changed and he doesn't have to leave until 6:00 P.M., how many more shows with breaks can the clown have?

    _____

4-8 • Guided Problem Solving

GPS **Student Page 207, Exercise 5:**

Lighting Lights are placed every $1\frac{3}{4}$ feet along both sides of a 14-foot driveway. How many lights are needed?

Read and Understand

1. Circle the information you will need to solve.

2. Which strategy can you use to answer this question?

   _____

   _____

Plan and Solve

3. Draw a number line to represent one side of the driveway. What will you use for intervals? _____

4. Start at zero. Plot a point for each light along the driveway. How many lights will there be? _____

5. Use your answer from Step 4 to write an expression for the total number of lights. _____

6. How many lights do you need total? _____

Look Back and Check

7. Can you think of another way to solve this problem?

   _____

   _____

   _____

Solve Another Problem

8. You are planting bushes every $2\frac{1}{4}$ feet along the side of a house that is $29\frac{1}{4}$ feet long. How many bushes do you need?

   _____

5-1 • Guided Problem Solving

GPS **Student Page 222, Exercise 36:**

Monuments The length of a side at the base of the Washington Monument is about $\frac{1}{10}$ of its height. The monument is about 555 feet tall. Find the length of a side at the base.

Read and Understand

1. What are you being asked to do?

   _____

2. Which word group tells you what operation to perform?

   _____

Plan and Solve

3. When multiplying a fraction by a whole number how do you rewrite the whole number?

   _____

4. Write an expression to solve the problem. _____

5. Simplify the expression. _____

6. Multiply the numerators, multiply the denominators, and simplify. _____

7. What is the length of a side at the base of the monument? _____

Look Back and Check

8. To estimate $\frac{1}{10}$ of 555, use compatible numbers. Find $\frac{1}{10}$ of 600. Is your answer reasonable?

   _____

Solve Another Problem

9. A concert hall has 12,360 seats. For the last concert, only $\frac{2}{3}$ of the hall was full. How many seats were unused?

   _____

5-2 • Guided Problem Solving

GPS Student Page 227, Exercise 18a:

A mother is $1\frac{3}{8}$ times as tall as her daughter. The girl is $1\frac{1}{3}$ times as tall as her brother. The mother is how many times as tall as her son?

Read and Understand

1. What are you being asked to do?

   _____

2. What do you do first when you multiply mixed number?

   _____

Plan and Solve

3. Write an equation for the sentence "A mother is $1\frac{3}{8}$ times as tall as her daughter," where m represents the height of the mother and d represents the height of the daughter.

   _____

4. Write an equation for the sentence "The girl is $1\frac{1}{3}$ times as tall as her brother," where d represents the height of the girl and b represents the height of the brother.

   _____

5. Substitute the expression for d from Step 4 for d in the equation you wrote in Step 3. _____

6. Simplify by multiplying the two mixed numbers. _____

7. The mother is how many time as tall as her son? _____

Look Back and Check

8. Divide $1\frac{5}{6}$ by either $1\frac{3}{8}$ or $1\frac{1}{3}$.

   _____

Solve Another Problem

9. Nora is building a birdhouse. The height of the birdhouse is $2\frac{1}{2}$ times the length of the birdhouse. If the length is $8\frac{2}{3}$ in. how tall is the birdhouse?

   _____

5-3 • Guided Problem Solving

GPS Student Page 233, Exercise 50:

Baking A recipe for a loaf of banana bread requires $\frac{2}{3}$ cup of vegetable oil. You have 3 cups of oil but need 1 cup for a different recipe. How many loaves of banana bread can you make with the rest of the oil?

Read and Understand

1. What are you being asked to do?

_____

_____

2. Explain how to divide fractions.

_____

_____

Plan and Solve

3. What number are you dividing by? Why?

_____

4. How many cups of oil are available
   to make the banana bread? _____

5. What number are you dividing? Why?

_____

6. Write a division expression to solve the problem. _____

7. Re-write the expression using multiplication. _____

8. Evaluate the expression. _____

9. How many loaves of banana bread can
   you make with the rest of the oil? _____

Look Back and Check

10. Multiply $\frac{2}{3} \times 3$. Does your answer check? _____

Solve Another Problem

11. Greg bought 24 bags of mulch for the planters in his front yard. If
    each planter uses $\frac{3}{4}$ bag, how many planters can he fill with mulch?

_____

5-4 • Guided Problem Solving

GPS **Student Page 238, Exercise 29:**

Construction A ceiling in an attic 24 feet wide needs insulation. Each strip of insulation is $1\frac{1}{3}$ feet wide. Estimate the number of insulation strips needed to fit the width of the attic.

Read and Understand

1. What are you being asked to do?

   _____

   _____

2. Which number(s) will you round to estimate?

   _____

Plan and Solve

3. To what number do you round $1\frac{1}{3}$?

   _____

4. Divide 24 by the rounded number. What is the result?

   _____

5. Approximately how many strips do you need?

   _____

Look Back and Check

6. How do you check your answer?

   _____

   _____

Solve Another Problem

7. A closet bar is $8\frac{3}{4}$ in. long. If a standard shirt is $1\frac{1}{2}$ in. wide, estimate how many shirts can you hang on the bar?

   _____

5-5 • Guided Problem Solving

GPS Student Page 244, Exercise 28:

Shopping You buy a shirt and a pair of pants. The price of the shirt is $\frac{5}{6}$ the price of the pants. The shirt costs $12.50. How much do the pants cost?

Read and Understand

1. What are you being asked to do?

   _____

2. Define a variable to represent the unknown.

   _____

3. Fill in the boxes with the correct information.

   ☐ · ☐ = ☐

Plan and Solve

4. Write an expression for the phrase
   "$\frac{5}{6}$ the price of the pants" if the pants cost p dollars. _____

5. How much does the shirt cost? _____

6. Write an equation to solve the problem. _____

7. What do you do to both sides of the
   equation to solve for p? _____

8. Solve the equation. _____

9. How much did the pants cost? _____

Look Back and Check

10. Determine if 12.50 is $\frac{5}{6}$ of 15.

    _____

Solve Another Problem

11. Lupe and Carlos are $\frac{1}{4}$ of the way done painting their new house.
    So far they have used $6\frac{2}{3}$ cans of paint. How many cans of paint
    will they use to paint the entire house?

    _____

5-6 • Guided Problem Solving

GPS **Student Page 248, Exercise 10:**

Estimate You spend $12.50 a year for a pass to school events. If you attend 7 events, is your cost more or less than $1.50 per event?

Read and Understand

1. What are you being asked to do?

   _____

   _____

2. What strategy is the best way to solve this problem?

   _____

Plan and Solve

3. How much did you pay for the pass?

   _____

4. How many events did you attend?

   _____

5. Write an equation to determine the cost of each event.

   _____

6. Is your cost more or less than $1.50 per event?

   _____

Look Back and Check

7. What is 7 × $1.50? Is your answer reasonable? Explain.

   _____

   _____

Solve Another Problem

8. A square kitchen floor has an area of 144 square feet. If you buy two-foot square ceramic tiles to cover the floor, how many tiles do you need?

   _____

   _____

5-7 • Guided Problem Solving

GPS **Student Page 252, Exercise 17:**

Prehistoric Creatures In 2001, scientists discovered the fossil of a huge crocodile. This crocodile was more than 40 feet long and weighed over 10 tons. A Nile crocodile can weigh $\frac{3}{4}$ ton. How many times as heavy as the Nile crocodile was the prehistoric crocodile?

Read and Understand

1. Which weighs more, the Nile crocodile or the prehistoric crocodile? Explain.

   _____

2. What are you being asked to do?

   _____

   _____

3. Define the variable for the unknown crocodile.

   _____

   _____

Plan and Solve

4. What is the least the prehistoric crocodile could weigh? _____

5. How much does the Nile crocodile weigh? _____

6. Write an equation for the question, " $\frac{3}{4}$ ton
   times what number is 10 tons?" _____

7. Solve the equation. _____

8. How many times as heavy as the
   Nile crocodile was the prehistoric crocodile? _____

Look Back and Check

9. Is $\frac{3}{4}$ times your answer equal to 10? _____

Solve Another Problem

10. Marie is 68 in. tall and her boyfriend Mario is 6 ft 2 in. tall. Who is taller? Explain.

    _____

5-8 • Guided Problem Solving

GPS Student Page 256, Exercise 27:

Costume Design A costume designer is making a costume for a figure skater. To make the legs, she needs two strips of fabric that are each 34 inches long. How many yards of fabric does she need to make the legs?

Read and Understand

1. Circle the information you will need to solve.

2. What are you being asked to do?

   _____

   _____

3. How many inches are in a yard?

   _____

Plan and Solve

4. How many strips of fabric does she need? _____

5. How long does each strip need to be? _____

6. How many inches of fabric do you need total? _____

7. How do you convert this into yards? _____

8. How many yards is it exactly?

   _____

9. How many whole yards of fabric does she need? _____

Look Back and Check

10. Approximately how many yards is each strip? Is your answer reasonable? Explain.

    _____

    _____

Solve Another Problem

11. Jessica is making fruit juice and it calls for 6 pints of water. Jessica only has a 2-quart pitcher. Will her fruit juice fit in the pitcher? Explain.

    _____

    _____

6-1 • Guided Problem Solving

GPS Student Page 271, Exercise 27:

Cats and Dogs The average adult cat has 30 teeth. The average adult dog has 42 teeth. Write the ratio of cat's teeth to dog's teeth in simplest form.

Read and Understand

1. What are you being asked to do?

   _____

   _____

2. What does "in simplest form" mean?

   _____

   _____

Plan and Solve

3. Which number goes in the numerator,
   cat's teeth or dog's teeth? _____

4. Which number goes in the denominator,
   cat's teeth or dog's teeth? _____

5. Write the ratio of cat's teeth to dog's teeth. _____

6. What greatest common factor do both the numerator
   and denominator have in common? _____

7. Rewrite the ratio using the greatest common factor. _____

8. Simplify the ratio. _____

Look Back and Check

9. Which have fewer teeth, cats or dogs? Does this agree with your
   ratio? Explain.

   _____

   _____

Solve Another Problem

10. The faculty softball league has 56 female players and 84 male players.
    Write the ratio of female players to male players in simplest form.

    _____

6-2 • Guided Problem Solving

GPS **Student Page 275, Exercise 19:**

Jump Rope Crystal jumps 255 times in 3 minutes. The United States record for 11-year-olds is 864 jumps in 3 minutes.

a. Find Crystal's unit rate for jumps per minute.

b. Find the record-holder's unit rate for jumps per minute.

c. How many more times did the record-holder jump per minute?

Read and Understand

1. What are you being asked to do in part *a* and part *b*?

   _____

   _____

2. What is a unit rate?

   _____

   _____

Plan and Solve

3. What is Crystal's rate? _____

4. What is Crystal's unit rate? _____

5. What is the record-holder's rate? _____

6. What is the record-holder's unit rate? _____

7. How many more times did the record-holder jump per minute?

   _____

Look Back and Check

8. How can you check your answer for parts *a* and *b*?

   _____

   _____

Solve Another Problem

9. Mike can make 60 egg sandwiches in 1.25 hours. What is his unit rate?

   _____

6-3 • Guided Problem Solving

GPS **Student Page 281, Exercise 24:**

Yogurt A flavor of frozen yogurt has 64 Calories in 2 ounces. How many Calories are in 5 ounces?

Read and Understand

1. Circle the information you will need to solve.

2. Will 5 ounces have more or less Calories than 2 ounces?

   _____

Plan and Solve

3. Write a ratio comparing 64 Calories and 2 ounces.

   _____

4. Write a ratio comparing an unknown amount of Calories and 5 ounces.

   _____

5. Write a proportion using the two ratios from Steps 3 and 4.

   _____

6. Find the value that completes the proportion.

   _____

Look Back and Check

7. Explain how to check your answer.

   _____

   _____

   _____

Solve Another Problem

8. 12 cans of chicken noodle soup contain 48 servings. How many servings do 8 cans of soup contain?

   _____

   _____

   _____

6-4 • Guided Problem Solving

GPS **Student Page 286, Exercise 26:**

Printing Your friend is having a poster printed from a photograph that is 4 inches wide by 6 inches tall. If the poster is 22 inches wide, how tall will the poster be if it is proportional to the photograph?

Read and Understand

1. Circle the information you will need to solve.

2. What does it mean to be *proportional*?

   _____

   _____

Plan and Solve

3. Write a ratio comparing 4 inches and 6 inches. _____

4. Write a ratio comparing 22 inches
   and an unknown length. _____

5. Write a proportion using the
   two ratios from Steps 3 and 4. _____

6. Use cross products to find the value
   that completes the proportion. _____

7. How tall will the poster be? _____

Look Back and Check

8. How can you check your answer? Does your answer check?

   _____

Solve Another Problem

9. You need to have a picture enlarged for a birthday party. The original picture is 3 inches high by 5 inches wide. You need the enlarged picture to be 15 inches wide. How long should the picture be if it is going to be proportional to the original picture?

   _____

6-5 • Guided Problem Solving

GPS Student Page 291, Exercise 19a:

Maps Suppose you redraw the map at the right using a scale of
0.5 centimeter : 1 centimeter. Does your drawing enlarge or reduce
the size of the map? Explain how you know.

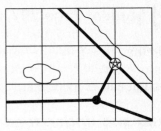

Read and Understand

1. What are you being asked to do?

   _____

   _____

2. What is a scale?

   _____

   _____

3. What scale are you going to use to redraw the map?

   _____

Plan and Solve

4. Does *0.5 centimeter* refer to the original map or the new map?

   _____

5. Does *1 centimeter* refer to the original map or the new map?

   _____

6. A length of 0.5 centimeter on the original map will be how long
   on your map?

   _____

7. Does your drawing enlarge or reduce the size of the map?

   _____

Look Back and Check

8. If your drawing is going to reduce the size of the map, give an
   example of a scale that would achieve this.

   _____

Solve Another Problem

9. You are going to redraw a painting exactly as it is in the original.
   What is the scale?

   _____

6-6 • Guided Problem Solving

GPS Student Page 297, Exercise 44:

Biology Ninety-nine percent of all kinds of plants and animals that have ever lived are now extinct. Write ninety-nine percent as a fraction and as a decimal.

Read and Understand

1. What percent of plants and animals are extinct?

   _____

2. A percent is a ratio of a number to what other number?

   _____

Plan and Solve

3. Ninety-nine percent means 99 out of what number?

   _____

4. Write this number as a fraction.

   _____

5. Which decimal place is the hundredths place?

   _____

6. Write ninety-nine percent as a decimal.

   _____

Look Back and Check

7. Explain how you can check your answer.

   _____

   _____

Solve Another Problem

8. Sixty-one percent of a school's students participate in extra-curricular activities. Write this number as a fraction and a decimal.

   _____

   _____

6-7 • Guided Problem Solving

GPS **Student Page 301, Exercise 19a:**

Vision In the United States, about 46% of the population wear glasses or contact lenses.

  a. In a a group of 85 people, how many people would you expect to wear glasses or contact lenses?

Read and Understand

1. Circle the information you will need to solve.

2. What are you being asked to do?

    _____

    _____

3. What method can you use to solve this problem?

    _____

Plan and Solve

4. Write 46% as a ratio. _____

5. Write a ratio comparing the unknown out of 85 people. _____

6. Write a proportion using the two ratios from Steps 4 and 5. _____

7. Solve the proportion for the unknown. _____

8. How many people would you expect to wear glasses or contact lenses? _____

Look Back and Check

9. How can you check your answer? Does your answer check?

    _____

    _____

Solve Another Problem

10. 77 percent of all band members received either an A or B on the last test. If this trend continues throughout the entire school of 1,260 students, how many students do you expect to receive A's or B's?

    _____

6-8 • Guided Problem Solving

GPS **Student Page 305, Exercise 26:**

Jobs Micah received the following tips. Estimate the value of each.

a. 20% of $14.20   b. 10% of $24.75

c. 15% of $19.70   d. Which tip was the greatest value?

Read and Understand

1. What is the easiest way to find 10% of an amount?

   _____

Plan and Solve

2. Estimate 10% of $24.75. _____

3. What is the relationship
   between 10% and 20%? _____

4. How do you use 10% in order to find 20%?

   _____

5. Estimate 20% of $14.20 _____

6. What is the relationship between 10%, 20%, and 15%?

   _____

7. How can you use 10% and 20% of an amount to find 15% of an
   amount?

   _____

   _____

8. Estimate 15% of $19.70

   _____

   _____

Look Back and Check

9. Which tip was the greatest value? Explain.

   _____

Solve Another Problem

10. Find 15% of $24.80 and determine if it is more or less than 20%
    of $22.40.

    _____

6-9 • Guided Problem Solving

GPS **Student Page 308, Exercise 13:**

Population According to the U.S. Census Bureau, the population of Illinois was 12,419,293 in the year 2000. Of the population, 26% was younger than 18 years of age. To the nearest hundred thousand, how many individuals in Illinois were *not* younger than 18 in the year 2000?

Read and Understand

1. What are you being asked to find?

   _____

   _____

Plan and Solve

2. What percent of the population was younger than 18 years old?

   _____

3. What percent of the population
   was *not* younger than 18 years old? _____

4. Which operation will you
   use to solve the problem? _____

5. Write an expression to find how
   many individuals in Illinois were
   not younger than 18 in the year 2000. _____

6. How many individuals in Illinois were
   not younger than 18 in the year 2000? _____

7. To the nearest hundred thousand, how
   many individuals in Illinois were *not*
   younger than 18 in the year 2000?   _____

Look Back and Check

8. Can you think of another way to solve this problem?

   _____

   _____

Solve Another Problem

9. It rained 15% of the days over a period of 32 days. How many days did it *not* rain?

   _____

7-1 • Guided Problem Solving

GPS Student Page 324, Exercise 20:

Number Sense The median of four numbers is 48. If three of the numbers are 42, 51, and 52, what is the other number?

Read and Understand

1. What are you being asked to do?

   _____

2. What is the median?

   _____

   _____

3. How do you find the median when there is an even number of data items?

   _____

Plan and Solve

4. Order the three numbers. _____

5. Between which two numbers does the missing number belong?

   _____

6. 48 is the number between the missing _____
   number and which other number?

7. What is the difference between the _____
   answer to Step 6 and 48?

8. What is the difference between the missing number and 48? Why?

   _____

9. What is the missing number? _____

Look Back and Check

10. Explain how to check your answer.

    _____

Solve Another Problem

11. The median of six numbers is 36. If five of the numbers are 29, 38, 34, 38, and 40, what is the other number?

    _____

7-2 • Guided Problem Solving

GPS Student Page 329, Exercise 14:

Speed Limits On a highway, the minimum speed allowed is 40 miles per hour and the maximum speed is 65 miles per hour. What is the range of speeds allowed on the highway?

Read and Understand

1. Underline the words that indicate which numbers you are to use to answer this question.

2. What is the range?

   _____

   _____

Plan and Solve

3. What is the least possible highway speed?

   _____

4. What is the greatest possible highway speed?

   _____

5. Write a subtraction expression to answer the question.

   _____

6. What is the range?

   _____

Look Back and Check

7. How can you check your answer? Does your answer check?

   _____

   _____

Solve Another Problem

8. You have to be at least 36 inches tall to ride the rides at Kiddie Land, but you cannot be any taller than 48 inches. What is the range of heights for these rides?

   _____

   _____

7-3 • Guided Problem Solving

GPS **Student Page 332, Exercise 4:**

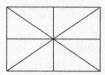

How many triangles are in the figure at the right?

Read and Understand

1. What are you being asked to do?

   _____

2. Which strategy will you use to solve the problem?

   _____

Plan and Solve

3. Label the corners of the rectangle A, B, C, and D starting with the upper left corner and going clockwise around the rectangle. Label the intersection in the center X.

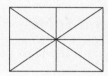

4. Label the midpoint lines F, G, H, and J, starting with the one between A and B.

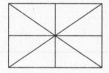

5. List the triangles that use only the points A, B, C, and D.

   _____

6. List the triangles that use only the points A, B, C, D, and X.

   _____

7. List the triangles that use any of the points.

   _____

   _____

8. How many triangles are there? _____

Look Back and Check

9. What other method could you use to count the triangles?

   _____

Solve Another Problem

10. How many rectangles are in the figure at the right?

    _____

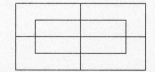

7-4 • Guided Problem Solving

GPS Student Page 338, Exercise 6:

Prime Ministers Make a bar graph to show how many years each prime minister was in office.

Gro Harlem Bruntland
Norway 13 years

Read and Understand

1. What is a bar graph?

   _____

   _____

Plan and Solve

2. If the bars are to be vertical, what should go along the horizontal axis?

   _____

Indira Gandhi
India 18 years

3. What should go along the vertical axis? _____

4. What is the maximum number of years?
   What scale should you use? _____

5. Draw the bar graph.

Golda Meir
Israel 5 years

Look Back and Check

6. What should you title your graph?

   _____

Solve Another Problem

7. Draw a bar graph to show how many of each pet the students at Moore Middle School have. 52 students have dogs, 68 students have cats, 22 students have birds, 15 students have lizards, and 4 students have rabbits.

Margaret Thatcher
UK 11 years

7-5 • Guided Problem Solving

GPS Student Page 344, Exercise 8:

Science The human body is made up of 21 chemical elements. Use the table at the right to make a circle graph.

Human Body Composition

Element	Percent
Oxygen	65
Carbon	18
Hydrogen	10
Nitrogen	3
Other	4

Read and Understand

1. How do you determine how much of the circle each element gets?

_____

Plan and Solve

2. Approximately how much of the circle should oxygen represent?

_____

3. Approximately how much of the circle should carbon represent?

_____

4. Approximately how much of the circle should hydrogen represent?

_____

5. Draw the circle graph.

Look Back and Check

6. Why should oxygen take up most of the graph?

_____

Solve Another Problem

7. The bake sale profits came from the sale of cookies (52%), brownies (24%), pies (12%), and cupcakes (12%). Make a circle graph to show the components of the bake sales profits.

7-6 • Guided Problem Solving

GPS **Student Page 349, Exercise 11:**

Wages Suppose your cousin works at a part-time job and earns $7 per hour. The spreadsheet shows a typical schedule for a week.

Write a formula for cell D2 and calculate the value in cell D2.

	A	B	C	D	E
1	Day	Time In (P.M.)	Time Out (P.M.)	Hours Worked	Amount Earned
2	9/15	3	8	?	?
3	9/17	4	8	?	?
4	9/19	3	6	?	?
5			Total:	?	?

Read and Understand

1. What are you being asked to do?

   _____

   _____

2. What does column D represent? _____

3. What does row 2 represent?

   _____

   _____

Plan and Solve

4. What operation do you use to figure the number of hours worked? _____

5. What cells do you need for the formula? _____

6. Write the formula for D2. _____

7. Calculate the value of D2. _____

Look Back and Check

8. Explain how you can check your answer.

   _____

Solve Another Problem

9. Your cousin's friend worked from 12 noon to 9 P.M. on 9/15. Create a row like your cousin's row 2 for his friend.

7-7 • Guided Problem Solving

GPS **Student Page 354, Exercise 10a:**

Heights The heights of nine people are given below.

5 ft 10 in.	4 ft 11 in.	5 ft 4 in.
5 ft 6 in.	6 ft 7 in.	5 ft 7 in.
6 ft 10 in.	5 ft 8 in.	5 ft 1 in.

a. Make a stem-and-leaf plot.

Read and Understand

1. Looking at the data, which numbers, the feet or the inches, should be the stems? Explain.

   _____

2. Looking at the data, which numbers, the feet or the inches, should be the leaves? Explain.

   _____

Plan and Solve

3. Order the heights from least to greatest.

   _____

   _____

4. Write the stems in order.
   Draw a vertical line next to the stems.

5. Write the leaves in order for each stem.

6. Include a key to explain what the stems and leaves represent. _____

Look Back and Check

7. How can you check to make sure you used all the data values?

   _____

Solve Another Problem

8. Eight friends were in a race. Their times are given below.

   1 min 48 s; 1 min 54 s; 2 min 20 s; 1 min 58 s; 3 min 2 s; 2 min 45 s; 2 min 30 s; 2 min 3 s

   Make a stem-and-leaf plot for the data.

7-8 • Guided Problem Solving

Reasoning How does the impression of a line graph change when you make the horizontal axis shorter but keep the vertical scale the same?

Read and Understand

1. What does a line graph look like?

   _____

2. What does it mean to "make the horizontal axis shorter"?

   _____

   _____

Plan and Solve

3. Graph the points $(1, 1)$ and $(2, 3)$ on the top graph to the right.

4. Graph the points $(1, 1)$ and $(2, 3)$ on the bottom graph to the right.

5. Compare the two lines from steps 3 and 4.

   _____

6. How does the impression of a line graph change when you make the horizontal axis shorter but keep the vertical axis scale the same?

   _____

   _____

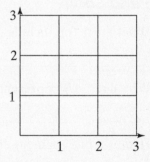

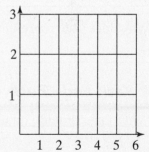

Look Back and Check

7. How did the scale on the x-axis change in step 4?

   _____

Solve Another Problem

8. How does the impression of a line graph change when you make the horizontal axis longer but keep the vertical axis scale the same?

   _____

   _____

8-1 • Guided Problem Solving

GPS Student Page 376, Exercise 32:

Writing in Math Explain why $\overline{AB}$ represents a line segment and $\overleftrightarrow{AB}$ represents a line.

Read and Understand

1. What is a line segment?

   _____

   _____

2. What is a line?

   _____

   _____

Plan and Solve

3. What must you include on a line when drawing a line in a plane?

   _____

4. Why does $\overleftrightarrow{AB}$ represent a line?

   _____

5. How is a line segment drawn differently?

   _____

6. Why does $\overline{AB}$ represent a line segment?

   _____

Look Back and Check

7. What facts should you use in explaining your answer?

   _____

Solve Another Problem

8. Explain why a ray is represented as $\overrightarrow{AB}$.

   _____

   _____

8-2 • Guided Problem Solving

GPS **Student Page 382, Exercise 16:**

Photography A 35-mm camera lens has a 45° viewing angle. What kind of angle is this?

Read and Understand

1. Underline the number(s) to use to answer this question.

2. List some different types of angles.

   _____

Plan and Solve

3. What is an acute angle?

   _____

4. What is a right angle?

   _____

5. What is an obtuse angle?

   _____

   _____

6. What is a straight angle?

   _____

7. What is the viewing angle of the 35-mm camera lens?

   _____

8. What kind of angle is this?

   _____

Look Back and Check

9. Why did you choose this type of angle?

   _____

Solve Another Problem

10. Chrissy is using brick pavers to line one corner of her front yard. The corner has a 120° angle. What type of angle is this? Explain.

   _____

   _____

8-3 • Guided Problem Solving

GPS Student Page 389, Exercise 21:

Architecture Before renovations, the Leaning Tower of Pisa stood at an angle of about 5° with a vertical line. What is the measure of the acute angle that the tower made with the ground? What is the measure of the obtuse angle?

Read and Understand

1. What is the first thing you are being asked to do?

   _____

   _____

2. What is the second thing you are being asked to do?

   _____

   _____

Plan and Solve

3. If the tower did not lean, what angle would the tower form with the ground?

   _____

4. By what angle measure from the vertical line was the tower leaning before the renovations?

   _____

5. Write a subtraction expression that you can use to find the acute angle.

   _____

6. What was the acute angle the tower made with the ground?

   _____

7. What was the obtuse angle the other side of the tower made with the ground?

   _____

Look Back and Check

8. How can you check your answer?

   _____

   _____

Solve Another Problem

9. A stop sign stands at an angle of 90° with the ground. During a snow storm, a car slid off the road and hit the sign so that it now forms a 62° angle with the ground. What is the obtuse angle formed on the other side of the sign?

   _____

8-4 • Guided Problem Solving

GPS **Student Page 395, Exercise 20:**

Sailing A triangular sail allows a boat to sail in any direction, even into the wind. Judging by its appearance, give all names possible for the triangle in the photo.

Read and Understand

1. Name the three ways you can classify a triangle by its angle measures.

    _____

2. Name the three ways you can classify a triangle by the number of congruent segments or sides.

    _____

Plan and Solve

3. Can a triangle be classified in more than one way? _____

4. Look at the picture of the sailboat. What appears to be true about the angle measures of the sail?

    _____

5. What appears to be true about the measures of the side lengths of the sail?

    _____

6. Classify the sail by the measures of its angles. _____

7. Classify the sail by the number of congruent sides.

    _____ _____

8. Give all possible names for the triangular sail.

    _____

Look Back and Check

9. Did you classify the triangular sail correctly?

    _____

Solve Another Problem

10. A sailboat has a sail shaped as shown. Judging by *its appearance*, give all names possible for the triangle in the diagram.

    _____

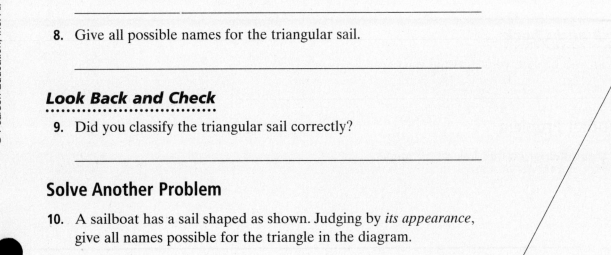

8-5 • Guided Problem Solving

GPS Student Page 399, Exercise 13:

Draw a parallelogram that has a 30° angle.

Read and Understand

1. What type of tool do you need to use to draw a 30° angle?

   _____

2. What do you know about the measures of opposite angles in a parallelogram?

   _____

Plan and Solve

3. What is the sum of the angles in a parallelogram? _____

4. How many 30° angles are there in the parallelogram? _____

5. What is the sum of the other two angle measures?

   _____

6. What is the measure of the two other angles?

   _____

7. Use a protractor to draw the parallelogram.

Look Back and Check

8. How can you be sure your drawing is a parallelogram?

   _____

Solve Another Problem

9. Draw a parallelogram that has a 110° angle.

8-6 • Guided Problem Solving

GPS Student Page 403, Exercise 7:

Collections Your friend decides to sort his collection of baseball cards. When he tries to put the cards in equal piles of two, he has one card left over. He also has one left over when he sorts the cards in piles of three or piles of four. But when he puts them in piles of seven, he has none left over. What is the least possible number of cards in your friend's collection?

Read and Understand

1. What does it mean that when he puts the cards in piles of seven, he has none left over?

   _____

   _____

2. What does it mean that when he puts the cards in piles of 2, 3, or 4, he has cards left over?

   _____

   _____

Plan and Solve

3. List the first 10 numbers divisible by 7, starting with 7.

   _____

4. Delete the even numbers. Which numbers remain?

   _____

5. Delete the numbers divisible by 3. Which numbers remain?

   _____

6. Divide these numbers by 2, 3, and 4. Which number only gives a remainder of 1?

   _____

Look Back and Check

7. Explain another way to do this problem.

   _____

   _____

Solve Another Problem

8. A teacher puts her students into groups. When she pairs the students, she has 1 student left over. When she groups them in 3s, she has 2 students left over. When she groups them in 4s, she has 3 students left over. Finally, when she groups them in 5s, she has none left over. If the school allows no more than 40 students in a class, how many students does the teacher have?

   _____

8-7 • Guided Problem Solving

GPS **Student Page 408, Exercise 18a:**

Triangles *MNO* and *PQR* are similar.

a. List the pairs of congruent angles.

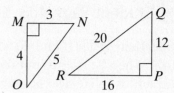

Read and Understand

1. What does it mean to be *congruent*?

_____

2. How do you know if the angles in triangles MNO and PQR are right angles?

_____

_____

Plan and Solve

3. Name the right angle in each triangle.

_____

4. Name the angle opposite the shortest side in each triangle.

_____

5. Name the angle opposite the second longest side in each triangle.

_____

Look Back and Check

6. How do you know if you paired the correct angles together?

_____

Solve Another Problem

7. List the pairs of corresponding sides in the figure above.

_____

8-8 • Guided Problem Solving

GPS Student Page 413, Exercise 19:

Reasoning How many lines of symmetry does a square have? Draw a diagram to support your answer.

Read and Understand

1. What is a line of symmetry?

   _____

   _____

2. What could you create that might help you to answer this question?

   _____

Plan and Solve

3. Draw a square and a line making a diagonal.

4. In the same square, draw a line making another diagonal.

5. In the same square, draw a line joining the midpoints of the opposite sides of the square.

6. In the same square, draw another line joining the midpoints of the opposite sides of the square.

7. How many lines of symmetry does a square have?

   _____

Look Back and Check

8. How do you determine if each line is a line of symmetry?

   _____

   _____

Solve Another Problem

9. How many lines of symmetry does an equilateral triangle have?

   _____

8-9 • Guided Problem Solving

GPS **Student Page 418, Exercise 23:**

What clockwise rotation of a figure will produce the same image as a counterclockwise rotation of 180°?

Read and Understand

1. What does it mean to rotate *clockwise*?

   _____

   _____

2. What does it mean to rotate *counterclockwise*?

   _____

   _____

Plan and Solve

3. What is the maximum number of degrees you can rotate an object?

   _____

4. If you add the number of degrees you rotate an object *counterclockwise* with the number of degrees that same object would be rotated *clockwise,* what would be the sum?

   _____

5. If an object is rotated *counterclockwise* 180°, what is the *clockwise* rotation?

   _____

Look Back and Check

6. How can you check your answer?

   _____

   _____

Solve Another Problem

7. What clockwise rotation of a figure will produce the same image as a counterclockwise rotation of 90°?

   _____

9-1 • Guided Problem Solving

GPS Student Page 434, Exercise 40:

Estimation The width of a door is about 1 meter. How can you estimate the length of a wall that contains the door?

Read and Understand

1. What are you being asked to do?

   _____

Plan and Solve

2. How wide is the door?

   _____

3. How can you use the width of the door to estimate the length of the wall?

   _____

   _____

   _____

   _____

   _____

   _____

Look Back and Check

4. What would be an approximate length of a wall in terms of the width of the door if about 6 doors would fit along the length of the wall?

   _____

Solve Another Problem

5. The height of a window is approximately 3 feet. How can you estimate the height of a wall that contains the window?

   _____

   _____

   _____

9-2 • Guided Problem Solving

GPS Student Page 438, Exercise 23:

Physics Light travels at approximately 299,792,458 meters per second. Approximately how many kilometers does light travel in one second?

Read and Understand

1. What are you being asked to do?

   _____

   _____

2. Which is larger, a meter or a kilometer?

   _____

Plan and Solve

3. How many meters does light travel in one second?

   _____

4. Will the number of kilometers light travels in one second be bigger or smaller than the answer in Step 3?

   _____

5. What number do you divide meters by to get kilometers?

   _____

6. Divide the answer in Step 3 by the answer in Step 5.

   _____

7. Approximately how many kilometers does light travel in one second?

   _____

Look Back and Check

8. How can you check your answer?

   _____

Solve Another Problem

9. A boulder weighs 44,320 grams. Approximately how many kilograms does the boulder weigh?

   _____

9-3 • Guided Problem Solving

GPS **Student Page 444, Exercise 21:**

Stamps The world's smallest stamp, shown at the right, measured 0.31 inch by 0.37 inch. Find the area of the stamp.

Read and Understand

1. What are you being asked to find?

   _____

2. What is the formula for the area of a rectangle?

   _____

Plan and Solve

3. What is the length of the stamp?

   _____

4. What is the width of the stamp?

   _____

5. Substitute the values into the formula.

   _____

6. What is the area of the stamp?

   _____

Look Back and Check

7. Explain how to check your answer.

   _____

   _____

Solve Another Problem

8. A window measures 28 in. wide by 36 in. tall. What is the area of the window?

   _____

9-4 • Guided Problem Solving

GPS Student Page 449, Exercise 25:

Algebra A parallelogram has an area of 66 square inches and a base length of 5 inches. What is the height of the parallelogram?

Read and Understand

1. What are you being asked to find?

   _____

2. What information are you given?

   _____

   _____

Plan and Solve

3. Write the formula you will use to find the area of a parallelogram.

   _____

4. Substitute the values you know into the formula.

   _____

5. What operation do you use to find the height?

   _____

6. What is the height of the parallelogram?

   _____

Look Back and Check

7. Check your answer. Explain your method.

   _____

   _____

Solve Another Problem

8. A parallelogram has an area of 96 cm and a height of 4 cm. What is the base length of the parallelogram?

   _____

9-5 • Guided Problem Solving

GPS **Student Page 454, Exercise 19:**

Hoops A dog trainer uses hoops with diameters of 24 and 30 inches. What is the difference between their circumferences? Use 3 for π.

Read and Understand

1. What do you need to know in order to answer the question?

   _____

2. How do you find the circumference of a circle when you know the diameter?

   _____

Plan and Solve

3. What is the diameter of each hoop?

   _____

4. What is the circumference of the 24 in. hoop?

   _____

5. What is the circumference of the 30 in. hoop?

   _____

6. What is the difference between their circumferences?

   _____

Look Back and Check

7. What unit should your final answer have? Why?

   _____

   _____

Solve Another Problem

8. Included in the china Jill and Ed received for their wedding were dinner plates and salad plates. The dinner plates have a diameter of 10 in. and the salad plates have a diameter of 7 in. What is the difference between their circumferences? Use 3 for π.

   _____

9-6 • Guided Problem Solving

GPS Student Page 458, Exercise 20:

Communications You can pick up the radio signal for station WAER FM 88 in Syracuse, New York, within a 45-mile radius of the station. What is the approximate area of the broadcast region? Use 3.14 for π.

Read and Understand

1. What are you being asked to find?

_____

2. Write the formula you use to find the area of a circle.

_____

Plan and Solve

3. What is the radius of the broadcast area?

_____

4. Substitute the values into the area formula.

_____

5. Evaluate the formula to find the area of the broadcast region to the nearest square mile.

_____

Look Back and Check

6. Use a radius of 50 and 3 for π to estimate the area. Then use a radius of 40 and 3 for π to estimate the area. Is your answer reasonable? Why?

_____

_____

_____

Solve Another Problem

7. The lead investigator in a search for a boat tells the coastguard to search everywhere within 5 miles of the last known location of the boat. What is the area of search region? Use 3.14 for π.

_____

_____

9-7 • Guided Problem Solving

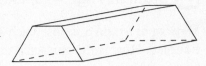

GPS Student Page 465, Exercise 24:

Name the figure. Then find the number of faces, vertices, and edges in the figure.

Read and Understand

1. What is a face?

   _____

2. What is a vertex?

   _____

   _____

3. What is an edge?

   _____

   _____

Plan and Solve

4. How many bases does the figure have? _____

5. Does this make the figure a pyramid or a prism? _____

6. What is the shape of the bases? _____

7. Name the figure. _____

8. How many faces are there total? _____

9. How many vertices are there? _____

10. How many edges are there? _____

Look Back and Check

11. How do you know the figure is not a pyramid?

   _____

Solve Another Problem

12. Name the figure. Then find the number of faces, vertices, and edges in the figure.

   _____

   _____

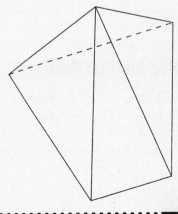

9-8 • Guided Problem Solving

Student Page 470, Exercise 15:

Writing in Math Suppose each dimension of a rectangular prism is doubled. How is the surface area affected?

Read and Understand

1. Write the formula used to find the surface area of a rectangular prism.

   _____

2. To double a number means to multiply that number by what value?

   _____

Plan and Solve

3. Multiply each dimension by 2 and substitute it into the surface area formula from Step 1.

   _____

4. Simplify the formula.

   _____

5. Instead of multiplying the area of each face by 2, multiply by what number?

   _____

6. How is the surface area affected when each dimension is doubled?

   _____

Look Back and Check

7. Explain another way to solve this problem.

   _____

   _____

Solve Another Problem

8. Suppose each dimension of a rectangular prism is tripled. How is the surface area affected?

   _____

   _____

9-9 • Guided Problem Solving

GPS **Student Page 475, Exercise 16:**

Trucks A rectangular truck bed has a length of 20 feet, a width of 8 feet, and a height of 7 feet. A cylindrical truck tank has a radius of 3.5 feet and a length of 22 feet. Find each volume. Use 3.14 for π.

Read and Understand

1. Circle the information you will need to solve the problem.

2. Write the formula used to find the volume of a rectangular solid and of a cylinder.

   _____

   _____

Plan and Solve

3. Substitute the values for the length, width, and height into the formula for the volume of a rectangular solid. What is the volume?

   _____

4. Substitute the values for the radius and length into the formula for the volume of a cylinder. What is the volume? Use 3.14 for π.

   _____

5. What are the units for the volume of a solid?

   _____

Look Back and Check

6. How can you check your answer?

   _____

   _____

   _____

   _____

Solve Another Problem

7. A silo is 32 feet tall and has a diameter of 12 feet. What is the volume of the silo? Use 3.14 for π.

   _____

9-10 • Guided Problem Solving

GPS Student Page 478, Exercise 4:

Entertainment At the Plex Cinema, every 15th customer gets a free ticket. Every 10th customer gets free popcorn. Of 418 ticket buyers, how many received both prizes?

Read and Understand

1. What are you being asked to find?

   _____

   _____

2. Which two problem solving strategies should you use to help you to solve this problem?

   _____

   _____

Plan and Solve

3. Find the common multiples of 10 and 15 between 1 and 100. Out of the first 100 customers, how many people won both prizes?

   _____

4. How many people out of 299 people are there who won both prizes? _____

5. Is 300 divisible by both 10 and 15? _____

6. How many people out of 418 people are there who won both prizes ? _____

Look Back and Check

7. Is your answer reasonable? Explain.

   _____

   _____

Solve Another Problem

8. Lara is working a double shift at the hospital. Every 30 minutes she drinks a glass of milk, and every 45 minutes she eats some grapes. If her shift is 15 hours long, how many times did she have both a glass of milk and some grapes?

   _____

10-1 • Guided Problem Solving

GPS **Student Page 494, Exercise 29:**

Starting at the fourth floor, an elevator goes down 3 floors and then up 8 floors. At which floor does the elevator stop?

Read and Understand

1. Circle the information you will need to solve the problem.

2. What are you being asked to do?

   _____

3. What is a good way to set up the problem visually?

   _____

Plan and Solve

4. At which floor does the elevator start?

   _____

5. When the elevator goes down 3 floors, at which floor does it stop?

   _____

6. When the elevator goes up 8 floors, at which floor does it stop?

   _____

7. At which floor does the elevator stop?

   _____

Look Back and Check

8. Write a numerical expression you can use to check your answer.

   _____

Solve Another Problem

9. A football team is on their opponents' 15-yard line. The quarterback throws a pass, but his team gets a penalty of 10 yards. During the next play, the quarterback passes the ball and the player runs the ball 8 yards. Which yard line is the team on for the next play?

   _____

10-2 • Guided Problem Solving

GPS **Student Page 501, Exercise 37:**

Temperature At 7:30 A.M. on January 22, 1943, the temperature was
−4°F in Spearfish, South Dakota. At 7:32 A.M., the temperature
had risen an amazing 49 degrees! What was the temperature then?

Read and Understand

1. Circle the information you will need to solve the problem.

2. What are you being asked to do?

_____

3. Which word tells you what operation to perform?

_____

Plan and Solve

4. What was the temperature at 7:30 A.M.?

_____

5. How many degrees did the temperature rise?

_____

6. What is the final temperature at 7:32 A.M.?

_____

Look Back and Check

7. What is the difference between 45°F and −4°F?

_____

Solve Another Problem

8. Jerry has a golf score of −3, or three under par. Sherry's score is
15 strokes, or points, *worse* than Jerry's score. What is Sherry's
score? (*Hint:* In golf, a *low* score is better than a *high* score.)

_____

10-3 • Guided Problem Solving

GPS Student Page 506, Exercise 30:

Hiking A hiker is at the top of Lost Mine Peak. The elevation of the peak is 6,850 feet. The beginning of the Lost Mine trail has an elevation of 5,600 feet. What is the trail's change in elevation?

Read and Understand

1. What are you being asked to do?

   _____

2. What operation do you use to represent change?

   _____

Plan and Solve

3. What is the elevation of the peak?

   _____

4. What is the elevation of the trail at the beginning?

   _____

5. Write an expression you can use to find the change in elevation.

   _____

6. What is the trail's change in elevation?

   _____

Look Back and Check

7. How can you check your answer?

   _____

   _____

Solve Another Problem

8. Sarah's savings account has $325 in it before she deposited her $255 paycheck. She then wrote the following checks: $20 for a parking ticket, $35 for her electric bill, $111 for her phone bill, $65 for her cable bill, and $89 for her new cell phone. Does Sarah have enough money left to buy a $150 DVD player? Explain.

   _____

10-4 • Guided Problem Solving

GPS **Student Page 511, Exercise 15:**

Ballooning Hot air balloons generally descend at a rate of 200 to 400 feet per minute. A balloon descends 235 feet per minute for 4 minutes. Write an integer to express the balloon's total movement.

Read and Understand

1. What are you being asked to do?

   _____

   _____

2. Which word describes the direction of the balloon?

   _____

3. Will the integer be positive or negative?

   _____

Plan and Solve

4. Each minute the balloon descends how many feet?

   _____

5. How many minutes is the balloon descending?

   _____

6. What is $235 \frac{\text{feet}}{\text{minute}} \cdot 4$ minutes?

   _____

7. Write an integer to express the balloon's movement.

   _____

Look Back and Check

8. What is 940 feet $\div 235 \frac{\text{feet}}{\text{minute}}$?

   _____

Solve Another Problem

9. A submarine dives for 5 seconds at 130 feet per second. Write an integer to express the submarine's movement.

   _____

© Pearson Education, Inc. All rights reserved.

10-5 • Guided Problem Solving

GPS Student Page 515, Exercise 22:

Stocks The value of a share of stock decreased $30 over the last 5 days. Find the average rate of change in dollars per day.

Read and Understand

1. Circle the information you will need to solve the problem.

2. What are you being asked to do?

   _____

   _____

3. What operation will you perform to find the answer?

   _____

Plan and Solve

4. How much did the stock decrease total?

   _____

5. How many days did you watch the stock?

   _____

6. What is the average decrease?

   _____

7. What integer represents the average decrease in dollars per day?

   _____

Look Back and Check

8. What is $-6 \cdot 5$? Does the answer make sense?

   _____

Solve Another Problem

9. Emma makes $18 per hour for providing technical support for an Internet provider. Emma works every day for 6 hours. After $2\frac{1}{2}$ months, how much will she make? (*Note*: Assume 1 month = 30 days.)

   _____

   _____

10-6 • Guided Problem Solving

GPS Student Page 520, Exercise 24:

Geometry A symmetrical four-pointed star has eight corner points. Seven of the points are $(-1, 1), (0, 3), (1, 1), (3, 0), (1, -1), (0, -3), (-1, -1)$. What are the coordinates of the missing point?

Read and Understand

1. What does *symmetrical* mean?

   _____

   _____

2. What is a good way to set up the problem visually?

   _____

Plan and Solve

3. What point is symmetrical to $(-1, 1)$ over the *y*-axis?

   _____

4. What point is symmetrical to $(-1, -1)$ over the *y*-axis?

   _____

5. What point is symmetrical to $(3, 0)$ over the *y*-axis?

   _____

6. What is the missing point?

   _____

Look Back and Check

7. Does the point $(-3, 0)$ form a four-point star with the other seven points?

   _____

Solve Another Problem

8. A five-pointed star that is symmetric over the *y*-axis has ten corner points. Eight of the points are $(-1, 1), (0, 3), (1, 1), (3, 1), (1, -1), (0, -1), (-2, -3), (-3, 1)$. What are the coordinates of the missing points?

   _____

10-7 • Guided Problem Solving

GPS Student Page 526, Exercise 16:

You receive a total of $125 for your birthday. You spend $20 on a sweater, $15 on a CD, $8 on a book, $12 on a pair of sunglasses, and $35 on a bicycle helmet. How much money do you have left?

Read and Understand

1. Circle the information you will need to solve the problem.

2. What are you being asked to do?

   _____

Plan and Solve

3. How much money did you receive?

   _____

4. How much money did you spend?

   _____

5. Write an expression for how much you have left.

   _____

6. How much money do you have left?

   _____

Look Back and Check

7. How can you check your answer?

   _____

   _____

Solve Another Problem

8. Helen received some cash for her birthday. She spent $14.30 on a CD and donated $25 to a charity. She put half of what was left into her savings account. She has $17.85 left. How much money did she receive on her birthday?

   _____

10-8 • Guided Problem Solving

GPS **Student Page 531, Exercise 21:**

Business Suppose you want to start a cookie business. You know that it will cost $600 to buy the oven and materials you need. You decide to charge $.75 for each cookie. The function $p = 0.75C - 600$ relates profit p to the number of cookies sold C.

  a. What will your profit or loss be if you sell 400 cookies? 500 cookies?

  b. How many cookies must you sell to break even?

Read and Understand

  1. What is *profit*?

    _____

    _____

  2. How will you use the equation to answer part *a* and part *b*?

    _____

    _____

    _____

Plan and Solve

  3. Substitute 400 for C and solve for p. What is the profit? _____

  4. Substitute 500 for C and solve for p. What is the profit? _____

  5. What value represents breaking even? _____

  6. Do you substitute this for p or C? _____

  7. How many cookies must you sell to break even? _____

Look Back and Check

  8. What is $(0.75 \cdot 800) - 600$? _____

Solve Another Problem

  9. Distance is a function of time. Suppose you walk at a rate of 2 miles per hour. Write an equation for the distance d if you walk for t hours and use it to determine the distance you will walk after 10 hours.

    _____

10-9 • Guided Problem Solving

GPS **Student Page 534, Exercise 4:**

Music Nate, Nina, Nancy, and Ned are in the school orchestra. Each person plays one of the instruments shown to the right. Nate does not play a wind instrument. Nina broke a string. Nancy sits next to the trumpet player, and Nate sits behind him. Which instrument does each person play?

Violin (string)

Clarinet (wind)

Read and Understand

1. What do you need to determine?

   _____

2. What problem solving strategy will you use?

   _____

Trumpet (brass)

Plan and Solve

3. You know that Nina broke a string. What instrument does Nina play?

   _____

4. You know that Nate does not play a wind instrument and he sits behind the trumpet player. What instrument(s) does this eliminate for Nate? What instrument does he play?

   _____

5. What instruments can you eliminate for Nancy? What does she play?

   _____

6. What instrument does Ned play?

   _____

Drum
(percussion)

Look Back and Check

7. Re-read the question. Did you match
   the person to the instrument correctly? _____

Solve Another Problem

8. Tom, Troy, Tia, and Ty all play either soccer, football, tennis, or baseball. The ball in Tom's sport is not round. Ty does not play tennis or soccer. Tia is not allowed to touch the ball with her hands except when it goes out of bounds in her sport. Who plays what?

   _____

   _____

11-1 • Guided Problem Solving

GPS **Student Page 550, Exercise 24a:**

Party A package of 25 party balloons has 8 red, 6 blue, 6 green, and 5 yellow balloons.

  a. Find the probability of selecting a yellow balloon at random. Write your answer as a fraction, a decimal, and a percent.

Read and Understand

1. What are you being asked to do?

   _____

   _____

2. What is probability?

   _____

   _____

Plan and Solve

3. What is the formula for determining the probability?

   _____

4. How many yellow balloons are there?   **5.** How many balloons of all colors are there?

   _____   _____

6. What is the probability of selecting a
   yellow balloon? Write your answer as a fraction. _____

7. Write the probability from Step 6 as a decimal. _____

8. Write the probability from Step 6 as a percent. _____

Look Back and Check

9. How can you check your answer?

   _____

   _____

Solve Another Problem

10. Find the probability of selecting a red balloon at random. Write your answer as a fraction, a decimal, and a percent.

   _____

11-2 • Guided Problem Solving

GPS Student Page 555, Exercise 11:

Basketball A basketball player makes 4 of 12 free throws. Find the experimental probability of the player missing a free throw.

Read and Understand

1. What are you being asked to do?

   _____

   _____

2. Which is experimental probability?

   _____

   _____

Plan and Solve

3. What is the formula for determining experimental probability?

   _____

4. How many trials are there?

   _____

5. How many times did he miss?

   _____

6. What is the experimental probability of the player missing a free throw?

   _____

Look Back and Check

7. Does the basketball player miss more or make more free throws? Does this agree with the probability you found?

   _____

   _____

Solve Another Problem

8. What is the experimental probability that he makes the free throw?

   _____

11-3 • Guided Problem Solving

GPS **Student Page 561, Exercise 22:**

A sample of 100 gadgets is selected from the day's production of 5,000 gadgets. In the sample, 7 are defective. Predict the number of faulty gadgets in the day's production.

Read and Understand

1. What are you being asked to find?

   _____

   _____

2. What do you need to use to solve this problem?

   _____

Plan and Solve

3. Write a ratio of the number of faulty gadgets to the number in the sample.

   _____

4. Let *n* represent the number of faulty gadgets in the day's production. Write a ratio of the number of faulty gadgets to the number in the day's production.

   _____

5. Create a proportion with the two ratios in Steps 3 and 4. Then solve the proportion.

   _____

6. Predict the number of faulty gadgets in the day's production.

   _____

Look Back and Check

7. Explain how to check your answer.

   _____

Solve Another Problem

8. A sample of 50 CDs is selected from the day's production of 300 CDs. In the sample, 4 are defective. Predict the number of faulty CDs in the day's production.

   _____

11-4 • Guided Problem Solving

GPS Student Page 566, Exercise 8:

Collecting Each box of a cereal brand contains one of four prizes. A box costs $3.50. You want to collect all four prizes. What is the least amount of money you may need to spend to get all four prizes?

Read and Understand

1. What are you being asked to find?

   _____

   _____

Plan and Solve

2. What is the probability of getting one of the prizes?

   _____

3. What is the least number of boxes you need to buy to get all 4 prizes?

   _____

4. If each box costs $3.50, what is the least amount of money it will cost you?

   _____

Look Back and Check

5. How likely is it that you get all four prizes in the first four boxes you buy?

   _____

Solve Another Problem

6. A fifth prize was added to the cereal boxes. What is the least amount of money you may need to spend to get all five prizes?

   _____

11-5 • Guided Problem Solving

GPS Student Page 572, Exercise 14:

Games To play a game, you spin a spinner and take a card. The spinner has equal sections that tell you to move 1, 2, 3, or 4 spaces. The cards read *Free Turn, Lose a Turn,* or *No Change.* Find the probability that you move 3 spaces and lose a turn.

Read and Understand

1. Before you find the probability, what do you have to find?

   _____

2. What are the two methods you can use to solve this problem?

   _____

   _____

Plan and Solve

3. How many outcomes are possible on the spinner? _____

4. How many outcomes are possible with the cards? _____

5. Using the counting principle, how may total outcomes are possible?

   _____

6. How many outcomes result in moving 3 spaces and losing a turn?

   _____

7. What is the probability that you move 3 spaces and lose a turn?

   _____

Look Back and Check

8. How would you use a tree diagram to answer this question?

   _____

   _____

Solve Another Problem

9. In this same game, what is the probability that you move 3 spaces and take any of the 3 cards?

   _____

11-6 • Guided Problem Solving

GPS Student Page 576, Exercise 14:

Fitness A body builder plans to do four different exercises in his workout. In how many ways can he complete his workout?

Read and Understand

1. What is a permutation?

   _____

   _____

2. What are some methods you can use to find the number of permutations?

   _____

Plan and Solve

3. How many choices does he have for his first exercise? _____

4. After he completes the first exercise, how many choices does he have for his second exercise? _____

5. After he completes the second exercise, how many choices does he have for his third exercise? _____

6. After he completes the third exercise, how many choices does he have for his fourth exercise? _____

7. Use the counting principle to find how many ways he can complete his workout?

   _____

   _____

Look Back and Check

8. Is you answer reasonable? How can you confirm your answer?

   _____

   _____

Solve Another Problem

9. The body builder pulled a muscle and can only do three different exercises in his workout. In how many ways can he complete his workout?

   _____

11-7 • Guided Problem Solving

GPS Student Page 582, Exercise 15:

Biology Assume two parents are equally likely to have a boy or a girl. Find the probability they will have a girl and then have a boy.

Read and Understand

1. What does it mean for two events to be equally likely?

   _____

2. How would you describe the events of having a girl and then having a boy?

   _____

Plan and Solve

3. What is the probability of a couple having a girl?

   _____

4. What is the probability of a couple having a boy?

   _____

5. Write an expression to find the probability of a couple having a girl and then having a boy.

   _____

6. Find the probability that a couple will have a girl and then have a boy.

   _____

Look Back and Check

7. List all of the possible outcomes of a couple having two children. What is the probability that they will have a girl and then a boy. Does your answer check?

   _____

Solve Another Problem

8. Find the probability that a couple will have a girl another boy, and then another girl.

   _____

12-1 • Guided Problem Solving

GPS Student Page 599, Exercise 29:

Commission *Commission* is pay earned as a percent of sales. Suppose a sales repesentative receives a weekly base salary of $250 plus a commission of 8% of her total weekly sales. At the end of one week, she earns $410. What is her sales total for the week? Use *s* to represent the total sales. Use the equation $0.08s + 250 = 410$.

Read and Understand

1. What is commission?

   _____

2. What are you being asked to find?

   _____

3. How will you use the given equation to solve the problem?

   _____

Plan and Solve

4. What is the first step in solving the equation?

   _____

5. Simplify both sides of the equation. _____

6. What is the second step in solving the equation?

   _____

7. Simplify both sides of the equation. _____

8. What is her sales total for the week? _____

Look Back and Check

9. How can you check your answer?

   _____

Solve Another Problem

10. During a holiday promotion the sales representative earned $650. What were her sales total for that week?

    _____

    _____

12-2 • Guided Problem Solving

GPS **Student Page 604, Exercise 22:**

Highway Safety Write an inequality for the sign shown at the right.

Read and Understand

1. What is an *inequality*?

   _____

   _____

2. What does the sign say without an inequality?

   _____

Plan and Solve

3. Is a 4-ton truck allowed?

   _____

4. Is a 2-ton truck allowed?

   _____

5. A truck has to weigh less than how much?

   _____

6. Write an inequality for the sign shown above.

   _____

Look Back and Check

7. What is another way to write this inequality?

   _____

Solve Another Problem

8. Write an inequality for the statement, "You must be at least 18 years old to vote."

   _____

12-3 • Guided Problem Solving

GPS Student Page 608, Exercise 29:

Budgeting Suppose you want to spend less than $30 total to buy two T-shirts and a pair of shorts. The shorts cost $13. Write and solve an inequality to find how much money you can spend on each T-shirt.

Read and Understand

1. What are you being asked to find?

   _____

   _____

2. Which symbol do you need to use in the inequality, < or >? _____

Plan and Solve

3. Given that that shorts cost $13, write an expression for the phrase "2 T-shirts and a pair of shorts." Let t represent the cost of one T-shirt.

   _____

4. Use the expression in Step 3 to
   write an inequality for less than 30. _____

5. What do you do first to both
   sides of the inequality?   _____

6. Simplify both sides of the inequality. _____

7. What do you do to both sides
   of the inequality to solve for t?   _____

8. What is the solution?   _____

9. How much money can you
   spend on each T-shirt?   _____

Look Back and Check

10. Can you spend exactly the amount you found in Step 9? Explain.

    _____

    _____

Solve Another Problem

11. Suppose you are able to spend $10 more. How much money can
    you spend on each T-shirt now?

    _____

    _____

12-4 • Guided Problem Solving

GPS Student Page 613, Exercise 6:

Skyscrapers The John Hancock Center in Chicago has twice as many floors as One Atlantic Center in Atlanta. The Sears Tower in Chicago has 110 floors, which is 40 floors less than the total number of floors in the other two skyscrapers. How many floors are in One Atlantic Center?

Read and Understand

1. What are you being asked to find?

   _____

2. Which strategy would be best suited to solve this problem?

   _____

Plan and Solve

3. How many floors does the Sears Tower have? _____

4. How many floors does the John Hancock and One Atlantic Center have in total? _____

5. What is the relationship between the number of floors at the John Hancock building and the number of floors at One Atlantic Center?

   _____

   _____

6. Write an expression for the sum of the heights of the John Hancock Center and the Atlantic Center

   _____

7. How many floors are in One Atlantic Center?

   _____

Look Back and Check

8. How can you check your answer?

   _____

   _____

Solve Another Problem

9. Amanda made some bracelets. She gave half of them to her friends. Then, she gave three to her sister. Her neighbor gave her four bracelets. She then sold half of the bracelets at a yard sale and had three left. How many did Amanda make?

   _____

12-5 • Guided Problem Solving

GPS **Student Page 619, Exercise 40:**

Egyptian Pyramids The area of the square base of the Great Pyramid at Giza is 52,900 square meters. What is the length of each side of the square base of the pyramid?

Read and Understand

1. How do you find the area of a square if you are told the length of the side?

   _____

2. What information are you given? What are you being asked to find?

   _____

   _____

Plan and Solve

3. What is the area of the square?

   _____

4. What is the square root of the answer to Step 3?

   _____

5. What is the length of each side of the square base?

   _____

Look Back and Check

6. How can you check your answer?

   _____

   _____

Solve Another Problem

7. The area of a square table is 1,296 in.^{2}. What is the length of each side of the table?

   _____

12-6 • Guided Problem Solving

Landscaping A landscaper needs to stake the tree at the right. A wire goes from the stake to a spot 40 ft up the trunk, as shown. How long must the wire be?

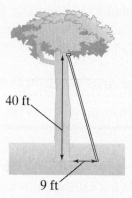

40 ft

9 ft

Read and Understand

1. What shape models the picture of the tree and the wire?

    _____

2. What theorem can be used to solve this problem?

    _____

Plan and Solve

3. Label the picture with the labels *a*, *b*, and *c*.

4. Substitute the values for *a*, *b*, and *c* into the formula.

    _____

5. Simplify both sides of the formula. _____

6. How do you solve for *c*?

    _____

7. What is *c*? _____

8. How long must the wire be? _____

Look Back and Check

9. How can you check your answer?

    _____

    _____

Solve Another Problem

10. Another tree needs to be staked that is 80 feet tall. The stake will be placed 18 feet from the tree. How long must the wire be for this tree?

    _____

    _____

Answers

Lesson 1-1

1. in the table   2. Compare the millions and see which is the least. Then compare the hundred thousands and see which is the least.   3. Braeburn   4. McIntosh   5. York   6. Empire
7. Braeburn, Empire, Idared, York, McIntosh   8. 2,198,000; 2,739,000; 2,753,000; 3,212,000; 3,304,000   9. Start with the smallest number. Compare it to each of the others until the numbers are ordered.   10. Philadelphia, San Francisco, Chicago, Los Angeles, New York City

Lesson 1-2

1. Less, because the word *and* is not used and the last number ends in "ths."   2. 3 decimal places   3. 0.   4. thousandths place   5. hundredths place   6. tenths place   7. 0.618
8. Sample answer: The number reads six hundred eighteen thousandths.   9. one and three hundredths centimeters

Lesson 1-3

1. 3 cities   2. Order the cities from least to greatest population.   3. 11.02 million, 11.7 million, 11.79 million
4. 11.02; 11.70; 11.79   5. 11.02   6. 11.79   7. 11.02, 11.70, 11.79   8. Jakarta, Indonesia; Delhi, India; Karachi, Pakistan
9. yes; 11.02 < 11.79 and 11.70 < 11.79   10. Anne, Jessie, Kara

Lesson 1-4

1. 283.5 grams; 9 balls; box; 595.34 grams   2. Estimate the total mass.   3. no; sample answer: to the nearest hundred
4. 300 grams   5. 2,700 grams   6. 600 grams   7. 2,700 + 600
8. 3,300 grams   9. grams   10. 12,000 grams

Lesson 1-5

1. Determine the population of Maine.   2. Subtract the population of each state from the total.   3. 12.66 million
4. 13.92 million   5. 13.92 − 12.66   6. 13.92 − 12.66 = 1.26
7. 1.26 million   8. Add 1.26 million to the total of the other states' population. The total should be 13.92 million.
9. your friend; 85.65 − 83.50 = 2.15; 2.15%

Lesson 1-6

1. Determine how long it takes for Clara to cut a log into 5 pieces.   2. It takes 12 minutes for 4 pieces, how long for 5 pieces?   3. longer, because she has to make another piece
4. 12 minutes   5. 12 minutes ÷ 4 pieces or 3 minutes per piece
6. 5 pieces × 3 minutes per piece or 15 minutes   7. because it takes 3 minutes to cut each piece; 3 minutes per piece × 5 pieces = 15 minutes.   8. $\frac{20}{15} = \frac{152}{x}$; $x = 114$ minutes

Lesson 1-7

1. the amount of calcium in one serving and the amount of calcium in 3.25 servings of cheddar cheese   2. determine the amount of calcium in 3.25 servings   3. multiply, because you know the amount of calcium in one serving and want to know

how much is in 3.25 servings   4. 0.2 gram   5. 3.25 servings
6. 0.2 × 3.25   7. 0.65 gram   8. more; 3.25 servings is more than one serving   9. 0.5 × 4.25 or 2.125 grams

Lesson 1-8

1. the swimming speed of a person and a dolphin
2. Determine the swimming speed of a person.   3. A dolphin, because a person swims 0.1 times as fast.   4. 27.5 miles per hour   5. 0.1 times as fast   6. multiply   7. one place
8. to the left   9. 2.75 miles per hour   10. less than
11. 0.1 × 60 or 6 miles per hour

Lesson 1-9

1. 0.9, 0.01, 25   2. Find how many pieces of paper are in the stack.   3. Determine if there is enough paper for each of 25 students to get three pieces of paper.   4. 0.01 centimeter
5. 0.9 centimeter   6. divide   7. 0.9 ÷ 0.01   8. 90 pieces of paper   9. 25 × 3 or 75 pieces of paper.   10. 75 < 90; yes
11. Sample answer: because 90 = 100 × 0.9   12. 5.4 ÷ 0.1 = 54; 54 baseball cards

Lesson 1-10

1. 312 coins total; one stack 15 inches tall; another stack 9 inches tall   2. Find the thickness of one coin to the nearest hundredth of an inch.   3. 24 inches tall   4. 24 inches tall
5. Divide.   6. 24 inches ÷ 312 coins or 0.077 inches
7. 0.077 inches per coin × 312 coins or 24 inches; yes
8. (7 + 13) ÷ 500 = 0.04; 0.04 inches

Lesson 2-1

1. Find how much it will cost to clean six items.   2. Use the pattern to determine which item is free.   3. finding the pattern
4. $3.50   5. $3.00   6. $2.50   7. $5.00 + $4.50 + $4.00 + $3.50 + $3.00 + $2.50 = $22.50   8. $2.00, $1.50, $1.00, $.50
9. the eleventh item   10. Yes; you could write a rule for the pattern.   11. $1\frac{3}{4}$ mi

Lesson 2-2

1. Find the number of bricks needed for a wall that is 22 feet long and 30 feet high.   2. the number of bricks needed
3. $N = 7 \times \ell \times h$ 4. 22 and 30   5. $N = 7 \times 22 \times 30$
6. $N = 4,620$ 7. 4,620 bricks   8. Divide your answer by 7 and see if the answer is 22 × 30, or 660. 4,620 ÷ 7 = 660, so the answer checks.   9. $S = (8 − 2) \times 180°$; $S = 6 \times 180°$; $S = 1,080°$

Lesson 2-3

1. Write an expression for how much the Sengs pay for admission to the zoo if they use the coupon.   2. the number of people in the Seng family   3. $3 per person, $5 off for a family, p people   4. $3   5. $3p$ 6. $3p − 5$ 7. yes; $−5 \times 3p$
8. $4r − 2$

Answers (continued)

Lesson 2-4

1. Find the number of possible different pairs. **2.** create an organized list **3.** 3 pairs **4.** 3 pairs **5.** 3 pairs **6.** Add the possible pairs for each trombone player. **7.** 9 pairs **8.** draw a diagram; yes, 9 pairs **9.** 18 different combinations

Lesson 2-5

1. Find the amount of carbon dioxide produced by burning 1 gallon of gasoline. **2.** You can use your knowledge of compatible numbers to determine the answer. **3.** 18 times what number is 360? **4.** 20 **5.** 20 times **6.** 20 lb
7. $360 \div 18 = 20$; this ratio should be the same for any amount of gasoline. **8.** $n = 1,872 \div 72$; each teacher has 26 students.

Lesson 2-6

1. Find how much money was in your wallet before you made any purchases. **2.** the amount of money in your wallet before the purchases **3.** total cost is $18.95; $7.05 left; how much money was in your wallet **4.** $18.95 **5.** $m - 18.95$ **6.** $7.05
7. $m - 18.95 = 7.05$ **8.** add 18.95 **9.** $m = 26.00$ **10.** $26.00
11. $26 - 18.95 = 7.05$; the answer checks **12.** $78 = 23 + s; s = 55

Lesson 2-7

1. Write and solve an equation to find the height of an adult female elephant whose hind footprint is 1.5 feet long.
2. elephant's height is; 5.5 times; length of hind footprint; 1.5 feet long **3.** It tells you to multiply. **4.** 1.5 feet
5. 5.5×1.5 **6.** $h = 5.5 \times 1.5$ **7.** 8.25 feet **8.** Divide the answer by 5.5 and see if the result is 1.5; the answer checks. **9.** $1.75 \times 38,200 = $66,850$

Lesson 2-8

1. Find how many cells there will be after 8 hours. **2.** It means the number is the product of a number multiplied by itself more than 2 times. **3.** 2^3 cells **4.** 2^4 cells **5.** 2^6 cells
6. 2^8 cells **7.** because the cell doubled eight times
8. 3^4 organisms

Lesson 2-9

1. Find the total number of sunflowers. **2.** 8 rows; Each row has 27 plants; total **3.** 8 rows **4.** 27 sunflowers **5.** 27×8
6. $27 \times 8 = 216$ **7.** 216 sunflowers **8.** Divide 216 by 8 and see if the answer is 27; the answer checks.
9. $(15 + 14) \times 8 = 232$ tiles

Lesson 3-1

1. Determine if the bill can be divided into 9 equal shares.
2. the divisibility rule for 9 **3.** If the sum of the digits of a number is divisible by 9, then the number is divisible by 9.
4. $56.61 **5.** 5, 6, 6, and 1 **6.** $5 + 6 + 6 + 1 = 18$ **7.** yes
8. yes **9.** Divide $56.61 by 9 to see if it divides evenly with no remainder. **10.** $1 + 3 + 7 = 11$; 11 is not divisible by 3; no

Lesson 3-2

1. Determine how many rows of guards are possible and how many guards will be in each row. **2.** the factors of 36 **3.** 9
4. 1, 2, 3, 4, 6, 9, 12, 18, 36 **5.** 1, 2, 3, 4, 6, 9, 12, 18, 36 **6.** 36, 18, 12, 9, 6, 4, 3, 2, 1 **7.** The row length times the number of people in each row should be 36. **8.** 1, 2, 3, 6, 9, 18; 18, 9, 6, 3, 2, 1

Lesson 3-3

1. Each person gets the same number. **2.** 20 cards **3.** No, 2 is not divisible by 3. **4.** 23 cards **5.** 27 cards **6.** 27
7. Brands B and C **8.** Brand B and C have 27 cards, which is divisible by 3. **9.** 5 rows of 9 drill team students and 5 rows of 5 color guard students

Lesson 3-4

1. Explain why the engineers wrote the driving time differently. **2.** They are the same. **3.** Sample answers: seconds, minutes, hours, days, weeks, months, years **4.** minutes
5. hours **6.** One engineer wrote the time in minutes and the other wrote it in hours. **7.** Sample answer: Time is more easily measured in minutes and hours in this situation.
8. $60 \times \frac{1}{4} = 15$; 15 minutes

Lesson 3-5

1. two slices; 50 guests, 12 slices **2.** Write the number of melons as a mixed number; then find how many whole melons are needed. **3.** 50 guests $\times 2 \frac{\text{slices}}{\text{guest}}$ or 100 slices **4.** 12 slices
5. division **6.** 100 slices $\div 12 \frac{\text{slices}}{\text{melon}}$ or $8\frac{1}{3}$ melons
7. 9 melons **8.** Parts of melons are not usually sold in bulk.
9. 321 students $\div 48 \frac{\text{students}}{\text{bus}}$ or $3\frac{11}{16}$; 4 buses

Lesson 3-6

1. fifteenth; fortieth **2.** Find which customer will be the first to get both a free CD and a free DVD. **3.** The 15th, 30th, 45th, 60th, 75th, 90th, 105th, 120th, 135th, 150th, etc. **4.** The 40th, 80th, 120th, 160th , 200th, etc. **5.** the 120th customer
6. Both 15 and 40 divide evenly into 120. **7.** Number of days until each volunteer works again: 5, 10, 15, 20, 25, 30; 6, 12, 18, 24, 30; 15, 30; Number of days until they work together: 30 days

Lesson 3-7

1. $12\frac{9}{20}$ ounces; $12\frac{7}{16}$ ounces **2.** Determine which drink is the better buy. **3.** which is bigger **4.** 80 **5.** $\frac{36}{80}, \frac{35}{80}$ **6.** $\frac{36}{80}$
7. the $12\frac{9}{20}$-ounce drink **8.** Change both mixed numbers to decimals and then compare them. **9.** Ana drove more miles because $\frac{1}{4} > \frac{1}{8}$.

Answers (continued)

Lesson 3-8
1. Rewrite the fraction $1\frac{1}{4}$ as a decimal. **2.** one divided by 4
3. 1.0 **4.** 0.25 **5.** $1.0 + 0.25 = 1.25$ **6.** 1.25 pounds
7. Write 1.25 as a fraction and see if it is the same as $1\frac{1}{4}$.
8. 3.75 pounds

Lesson 3-9
1. every 40 minutes; first train; 5:00 A.M.; closest; 12:35 P.M.
2. Find the department time closest to 12:35 P.M. **3.** 5:00,
5:40, 6:20, 7:00, 7:40, 8:20, 9:00, 9:40 **4.** The odd hours have 2
departures, on the hour and forty minutes after the hour. The
even hours have one departure at 20 minutes after the hour.
5. even **6.** 2 **7.** 12:00 P.M. and 12:40 P.M. **8.** 12:40 P.M.
9. List all of the departure times starting at 5:00 P.M.
10. 7:15, 7:30, 7:45, 8:00, 8:15, etc.; 10:30 A.M. is closest to 10:25.

Lesson 4-1
1. Estimate the total width of the coins. **2.** to estimate the
width of the coins **3.** $\frac{11}{16}$ in. **4.** $\frac{1}{2}$ in. **5.** $\frac{11}{16}$ in., $\frac{13}{16}$ in., $\frac{3}{4}$ in.,
and $\frac{15}{16}$ in. **6.** 1 in. **7.** 1 in. **8.** 1 in. **9.** $\frac{1}{2} + 1 + 1 + 1$; $3\frac{1}{2}$ in.
10. More; the estimates were rounded up.
11. $4 + 1\frac{1}{2} + 3 + 4\frac{1}{2} = 13$; 13 in.

Lesson 4-2
1. Determine how much of your blood is plasma.
2. subtraction **3.** $\frac{11}{20}$ **4.** $\frac{9}{20}$ **5.** $\frac{11}{20} - \frac{9}{20}$ **6.** $\frac{2}{20}$ or $\frac{1}{10}$
7. Add $\frac{9}{20}$ and the answer and see if the sum is $\frac{11}{20}$.
8. $16\frac{5}{8} - 15\frac{3}{8} = 1\frac{1}{4}$; $1\frac{1}{4}$ inches

Lesson 4-3
1. In part a, you estimate the total rainfall; in part b, you find
the actual sum. **2.** 0; 1 inch **3.** $0 + 1 = 1$ inch **4.** common
denominator **5.** 40 **6.** $\frac{12}{40}; \frac{35}{40}$ **7.** $\frac{47}{40}$ or $1\frac{7}{40}$ inches of rainfall
8. Yes, because $1\frac{7}{40}$ is close to 1.
9. Sample answer: $1 + 0 + 1 + \frac{1}{2} = 2\frac{1}{2}$; $2\frac{1}{8}$ cups

Lesson 4-4
1. $4\frac{11}{12}$ feet; $2\frac{3}{4}$ feet; how deep **2.** addition **3.** 12
4. $4\frac{11}{12}$ feet and $2\frac{9}{12}$ feet **5.** $4\frac{11}{12}$ feet $+ 2\frac{9}{12}$ feet
6. $6\frac{20}{12} = 7\frac{8}{12} = 7\frac{2}{3}$ feet **7.** Sample answer: Subtract $4\frac{11}{12}$ feet
from $7\frac{2}{3}$ feet and see if the answer is $2\frac{3}{4}$ feet. **8.** No, it is not
quite 30 feet.

Lesson 4-5
1. $15\frac{3}{4}$ inches; $18\frac{1}{2}$ inches; difference **2.** Find the difference
in the snowfall amounts. **3.** $15\frac{3}{4}$ inches **4.** $18\frac{1}{2}$ inches
5. 4 **6.** $15\frac{3}{4}, 18\frac{2}{4}$ **7.** $2\frac{3}{4}$ inches **8.** Sample answer: Add $15\frac{3}{4}$
and $2\frac{3}{4}$; the answer should be $18\frac{2}{4}$. **9.** $\frac{14}{6} - 2(\frac{5}{6}) = \frac{14}{6} -$
$\frac{10}{6} = \frac{4}{6} = \frac{2}{3} \div 2 = \frac{1}{3}$ yard

Lesson 4-6
1. 10-yard, $5\frac{2}{3}$ yards, $3\frac{3}{4}$ yards **2.** Add the two lengths of
edging and subtract from 10 yards. **3.** $5\frac{2}{3}$ yards, $3\frac{3}{4}$ yards
4. $9\frac{5}{12}$ yards **5.** 10 yards **6.** $\frac{7}{12}$ yard **7.** Add all of the
numbers; the answer is 10 yards. **8.** $1\frac{5}{12}$ yards

Lesson 4-7
1. 45-minute; begin at 10:00 A.M.; leave the third party by
2:15 P.M.; leave one hour between **2.** Create a schedule.
3. Create a table or work backward. **4.** 10:45 A.M.
5. 11:45 A.M. **6.** 12:30 P.M. **7.** 1:30 P.M. **8.** 2:15 P.M. **9.** yes
10. 3:15–4:00, 5:00–5:45; 2 more shows

Lesson 4-8
1. $1\frac{3}{4}$ feet; 14-foot driveway **2.** Draw a diagram.
3. $\frac{1}{4}$ ft

```
+--+--+--+--+--+--+--+--+--+--+--+--+--+--+
0  1  2  3  4  5  6  7  8  9  10 11 12 13 14
```

4. 9 lights

```
+--+--+--+--+--+--+--+--+--+--+--+--+--+--+
0  1  2  3  4  5  6  7  8  9  10 11 12 13 14
```

5. total $= 9 \times 2$
6. 18 lights **7.** Sample answer: Use the equation $14 \div 1\frac{3}{4} + 1$
to find the number of lights on one side of the driveway.
8. $29\frac{1}{4} \div 2\frac{1}{4} + 1 = 14$; 14 bushes

Lesson 5-1
1. Find the length of a side at the base. **2.** The words "$\frac{1}{10}$ of
its height" tell you to multiply. **3.** Write it as a fraction with a
denominator of 1. **4.** $\frac{1}{10} \times \frac{555}{1}$
5. $\frac{1}{(5 \cdot 2)} \times \frac{(5 \cdot 111)}{1} = \frac{1}{2} \times \frac{111}{1}$ **6.** $\frac{111}{2} = 55\frac{1}{2}$ **7.** 55.5 feet
8. 60; yes **9.** 4,120 seats

Lesson 5-2
1. Find how many times taller the mother is than her son.
2. Rewrite each number as an improper fraction.
3. $m = 1\frac{3}{8}d$ **4.** $d = 1\frac{1}{3}b$ **5.** $m = (1\frac{3}{8})(1\frac{1}{3}b)$
6. $m = (\frac{11}{8})(\frac{4}{3})b = 1\frac{5}{6}b$ **7.** $1\frac{5}{6}$
8. $1\frac{5}{6} \div 1\frac{3}{8} = 1\frac{1}{3}$; $1\frac{5}{6} \div 1\frac{1}{3} = 1\frac{3}{8}$ **9.** $8\frac{2}{3} \times 2\frac{1}{2}$ or $21\frac{2}{3}$ in.

Answers (continued)

Lesson 5-3

1. Find how many loaves of banana bread you can make with the rest of the oil. **2.** Multiply the first fraction by the reciprocal of the divisor. **3.** $\frac{2}{3}$ cup; the recipe needs $\frac{2}{3}$ cup of oil. **4.** 2 cups **5.** 2 cups; that is the amount of oil available. **6.** $2 \div \frac{2}{3}$ **7.** $2 \cdot \frac{3}{2}$ **8.** $2 \cdot \frac{3}{2} = \frac{2}{1} \cdot \frac{3}{2} = \frac{3}{1} = 3$ **9.** 3 loaves **10.** 2; yes **11.** $24 \div \frac{3}{4}$ or 32 planters

Lesson 5-4

1. Estimate the number of strips of insulation needed to fit the width of the attic. **2.** $1\frac{1}{3}$ **3.** 1 **4.** 24 **5.** 24 strips **6.** Divide 24 by $1\frac{1}{3}$ to see if it is close to the estimate. **7.** $8\frac{3}{4} \approx 10$; $1\frac{1}{2} \approx 2$; $10 \div 2$ or 5 shirts

Lesson 5-5

1. Find the cost of the pants. **2.** Sample answer: Let $p =$ the cost of the pants. **3.** $\boxed{\frac{5}{6}} \cdot \boxed{p} = \boxed{12.50}$ **4.** $\frac{5}{6}p$
5. $12.50 **6.** $\frac{5}{6}p = 12.50$ **7.** Multiply by $\frac{6}{5}$
8. $p = \frac{6}{5}(12.50) = 15$ **9.** $15 **10.** Sample answer: Yes; $\frac{5}{6} \times 15 = 12.50$. **11.** $\frac{1}{4}p = 6\frac{2}{3}$; $p = 26\frac{2}{3}$; $26\frac{2}{3}$ cans

Lesson 5-6

1. Determine how much it costs per event if you attend 7 events. **2.** Write an equation. **3.** $12.50 **4.** 7 **5.** $12.50 $\div$ 7 = $1.79 **6.** more **7.** $10.50; yes; seven events at $1.50 is $10.50, so it must cost more than $1.50 for each event. **8.** $144 \div (2 \times 2) = 144 \div 4 = 36$; 36 tiles

Lesson 5-7

1. The prehistoric crocodile; 10 tons $> \frac{3}{4}$ ton. **2.** Find how many times heavier the prehistoric crocodile was than the Nile crocodile. **3.** Sample answer: Let $n =$ number of times heavier the prehistoric crocodile is. **4.** 10 tons **5.** $\frac{3}{4}$ ton **6.** $\frac{3}{4}n = 10$ **7.** $\frac{3}{4}n = 10$; $3n = 40$; $n = 13.\overline{3}$ **8.** $13.\overline{3}$ times **9.** $\frac{3}{4} \times 13\frac{1}{3} = \frac{3}{4} \times \frac{40}{3} = 10$; yes **10.** Mario is taller because Marie is 5 ft 8 in. tall.

Lesson 5-8

1. two strips; 34 inches; How many yards **2.** Find how many yards of fabric she needs to make the legs. **3.** 36 inches = 1 yard **4.** 2 strips **5.** 34 in. **6.** 68 in. **7.** Divide by 36. **8.** $\frac{68}{36} = \frac{17}{9} = 1.\overline{8}$ yards **9.** 2 yards **10.** 1 yard; yes, if each leg is approximately 1 yard, then 2 yards of material are needed. **11.** Two quarts is only 4 pints, so her pitcher is not big enough for 6 pints.

Lesson 6-1

1. Write the ratio of cat's teeth to dog's teeth in simplest form. **2.** The numerator and denominator have no common factors other than one. **3.** cat's teeth **4.** dog's teeth **5.** $\frac{30}{42}$ **6.** 6 **7.** $\frac{5 \cdot 6}{7 \cdot 6}$ **8.** $\frac{5 \cdot 6}{7 \cdot 6} = \frac{5}{7}$ **9.** Cats; yes, because the numerator is smaller than the denominator. **10.** $\frac{56}{84} = \frac{8}{12} = \frac{2}{3}$

Lesson 6-2

1. Find Crystal's unit rate. Find the record-holder's unit rate. **2.** The rate for one unit of a given quantity is called the unit rate. **3.** 255 jumps in 3 minutes **4.** $\frac{255}{3}$ or 85 jumps per minute **5.** 864 jumps in 3 minutes **6.** $\frac{864}{3}$ or 288 jumps per minute **7.** 288 – 85 or 203 times **8.** The unit rate times 3 should equal the original rate. **9.** $\frac{60}{1.25}$ or 48 sandwiches per hour

Lesson 6-3

1. 64 Calories; 2 ounces; 5 ounces **2.** more **3.** $\frac{64}{2}$ **4.** $\frac{x}{5}$ **5.** $\frac{64}{2} = \frac{x}{5}$ **6.** 160 Calories **7.** $\frac{64}{2} = \frac{160}{5} = 32$ **8.** $\frac{12}{48} = \frac{8}{x}$; $x = 32$; 32 servings

Lesson 6-4

1. 4 inches wide; 6 inches tall; 22 inches wide; how tall **2.** The two ratios on either side of the proportion are equal. **3.** $\frac{4}{6}$ **4.** $\frac{22}{x}$ **5.** $\frac{4}{6} = \frac{22}{x}$ **6.** 33 **7.** 33 inches **8.** $\frac{4}{6} = \frac{22}{33} = \frac{2}{3}$; yes **9.** $\frac{3}{5} = \frac{x}{15}$; $x = 9$; 9 inches

Lesson 6-5

1. Determine if your drawing will enlarge or reduce the size of the map. **2.** The ratio that compares a length in a drawing or model to the length in the original object. **3.** 0.5 centimeter : 1 centimeter **4.** original map **5.** new map **6.** 1 centimeter **7.** enlarge **8.** 1 centimeter = 0.5 centimeter **9.** 1 : 1

Lesson 6-6

1. 99% **2.** 100 **3.** 100 **4.** $\frac{99}{100}$ **5.** two places to the right of the decimal **6.** 0.99 **7.** Divide 99 by 100 and see if the answer equals 0.99. **8.** $\frac{61}{100}$; 0.61

Lesson 6-7

1. 46%; of 85; how many people **2.** Find the number of people out of 85 who would wear glasses or lenses. **3.** Write and solve a proportion. **4.** $\frac{46}{100}$ **5.** $\frac{x}{85}$ **6.** $\frac{46}{100} = \frac{x}{85}$ **7.** $x = 39.1$ **8.** 39 people **9.** Divide 39 by 85 or approximately 0.46; yes **10.** 970 students

Courses 3 Guided Problem Solving

Answers (continued)

Lesson 6-8

1. Move the decimal point to the left one place.   **2.** $2.48
3. 20% is 10% doubled.   **4.** Find 10% first and then double the answer.   **5.** $1.42 × 2 = $2.84   **6.** 15% is halfway between 10% and 20%.   **7.** Find 10% and 20% then find the number that is halfway between the two numbers.
8. $1.97 ≈ $2; $3.94 ≈ $4; halfway between $2 and $4 is $3
9. 15% of $19.70; compare $2.84, $2.48, and $3.   **10.** $3.72; $4.48; it is less.

Lesson 6-9

1. Find how many individuals in Illinois were not younger than 18 in the year 2000.   **2.** 26%   **3.** 74%   **4.** multiplication
5. 0.74 × 12,419,293   **6.** 9,190,277 people   **7.** 9,200,000 people   **8.** Find 26% of 12,419,293. Subtract that value from 12,419,293.   **9.** 0.85 × 32 = 27 days

Lesson 7-1

1. Find the fourth number.   **2.** The median is the middle number in a set of ordered data.   **3.** You add the two middle numbers and divide by 2.   **4.** 42, 51, 52   **5.** 42 and 51 since 48 > 42 and 48 < 51.   **6.** 51   **7.** 3   **8.** 3; 48 is halfway between 42 and 51.   **9.** 48 − 3 or 45   **10.** (45 + 51) ÷ 2 = 96 ÷ 2 = 48
11. 29, 34, 38, 38, 40; (34 + 38) ÷ 2 = 72 ÷ 2 = 36; 30

Lesson 7-2

1. minimum; maximum   **2.** The range is the difference between the least and the greatest values.   **3.** 40 mi/h
4. 65 mi/h   **5.** 65 − 40 = 25   **6.** 25 mi/h   **7.** Find the sum of 25 and 40 and see it equals 65; yes.   **8.** 48 − 36 = 12; 12 inches

Lesson 7-3

1. Find how many triangles there are in the figure.
2. Make an organized list.
3.

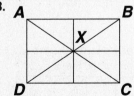

4.

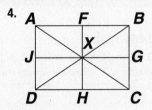

5. ABC, ABD, BCD, ACD   **6.** AXB, BXC, CXD, AXD
7. AFX, BFX, BXG, GXC, CXH, HXD, DXJ, JXA, ABC, ABD, BCD, ACD, AXB, BXC, CXD, AXD   **8.** 16
9. Solve a simpler problem or look for a pattern.
10. 18 rectangles

Lesson 7-4

1. A bar graph uses vertical or horizontal bars to display numerical information.   **2.** the names of the prime ministers
3. the number of years   **4.** 18; one mark = 2 years
5. Sample answer:

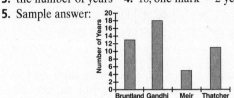

6. Prime Ministers' Time in Office
7.

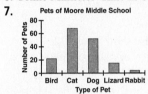

Lesson 7-5

1. Use number sense to estimate.   **2.** more than half but less than three-quarters   **3.** less than one-quarter   **4.** less than half of one-quarter
5. Human Body Composition   **6.** It accounts for more than 50%.
7. Bake Sale Profits

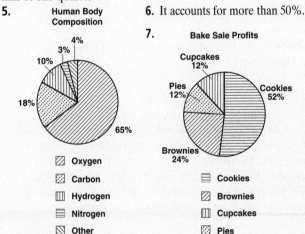

Lesson 7-6

1. Write a formula for a spreadsheet cell and calculate its value.   **2.** the number of hours worked   **3.** the date (9/15), the time in (3 P.M.), and the time out (8 P.M.).   **4.** subtraction
5. B2 and C2   **6.** D2 = C2 − B2   **7.** 8 − 3 = 5; 5 hours
8. Add 5 and 3 or subtract 5 from 8.
9.

A	B	C	D	E
9/15	12	9	9	$63

Answers (continued)

Lesson 7-7

1. feet, because those numbers are read first   2. inches, because those numbers are read second   3. 4 ft 11 in., 5 ft 1in., 5 ft 4 in., 5 ft 6 in., 5 ft 7 in., 5 ft 8 in., 5 ft 10 in., 6 ft 7 in., 6 ft 10 in.

4.
4	
5	
6	

5.
4	11
5	1 4 6 7 8 10
6	7 10

6. Key: 4|11 means 4 ft 11 in.   7. Count them; there are 9 values.   8. Key: 1|48 means 1 min 48 s

1	48 54 58
2	3 20 30 45
3	2

Lesson 7-8

1. It is a graph of line segments that show trends.   2. The scale on the horizontal axis is closer together than the scale on the vertical axis.   3.

4.

5. The line in step 4 is steeper.   6. The impression is that the increase occurs at a faster rate.   7. The scale got shorter.   8. The impression is that the increase occurs at a slower rate.

Lesson 8-1

1. A line segment is part of a line with two endpoints.
2. A line is a series of points that extends indefinitely in two opposite directions.   3. arrows   4. The line above the endpoints has arrows.   5. A line segment has endpoints, not arrows.   6. The line above the endpoints has endpoints.
7. the definition of line segment and line   8. A ray has one endpoint and extends indefinitely in one direction.

Lesson 8-2

1. 45°   2. Sample answer: acute, right, obtuse, straight
3. an angle whose measure is between 0° and 90°   4. an angle whose measure is 90°   5. an angle whose measure is between 90° and 180°   6. an angle whose measure is 180°   7. 45°
8. acute angle   9. The 45° viewing angle is between 0° and 90°.   10. Obtuse angle, because the corner is more than 90° and less than 180°.

Lesson 8-3

1. Find the measure of the acute angle that the tower made with the ground.   2. Find the measure of the obtuse angle that the tower made with the ground.   3. 90°   4. 5°
5. 90 − 5 = 85   6. 85°   7. 180 − 85 = 95; 95°   8. Add the two angle measures to see if they equal 180°.
9. 180 − 62 = 118; the obtuse angle formed is 118°.

Lesson 8-4

1. acute, obtuse, right   2. equilateral, isosceles, scalene
3. yes   4. The angles appear to be the same measure.
5. The lengths appear to be congruent.   6. acute triangle
7. equilateral or isosceles triangle 8. acute equilateral; acute isosceles 9. yes   10. right scalene

Lesson 8-5

1. a protractor   2. They are equal.   3. 360°   4. 2   5. 360 − (2 × 30) = 300; 300°   6. Sample answer: 300 ÷ 2 = 150; 150°
7. Sample drawing:

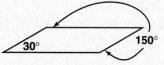

8. The opposite sides should be parallel.

9. Sample drawing:

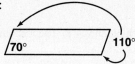

Lesson 8-6

1. It means that 7 divides evenly into the number of cards that he has.   2. It means the number of cards he has is not divisible by 2, 3, or 4.   3. 7, 14, 21, 28, 35, 42, 49, 56, 63, 70
4. 7, 21, 35, 49, 63   5. 7, 35, 49   6. 49   7. Divide the multiples of 7 by 2, 3, and 4 to see which quotients have a remainder of one card.   8. 35 students

Lesson 8-7

1. to be the same   2. There is a square drawn at the vertex of the angle.   3. ∠NMO; ∠QPR   4. ∠NOM; ∠QRP
5. ∠MNO; ∠RQP   6. They are opposite their corresponding sides.   7. $\overline{MN}, \overline{PQ}; \overline{MO}, \overline{PR}; \overline{ON}, \overline{RQ}$

Lesson 8-8

1. If you fold a drawing on its line of symmetry, the two sides match.   2. Create a square out of paper and fold it.
3.   4.   5.

6.

7. 4 lines of symmetry

8. If you fold the square along the line, each half should match.
9. 3 lines of symmetry

Answers (continued)

Lesson 8-9

1. to rotate around the circle, like a clock hand, to the right
2. To rotate around the circle, opposite to the direction a clock hand moves, to the left. **3.** 360° **4.** 360° **5.** 180°
6. Add the two degree measures; the sum should equal 360°.
7. 360 − 90 = 270; 270°

Lesson 9-1

1. Estimate the length of the wall. **2.** about 1 m
3. Method 1: Estimate how many doors would fit along the wall. Then multiply that value by 1 m. Method 2: Use a piece of string whose width matches the width of the door. See how many times you can lay the string end-to-end from one end of the wall to the other end. **4.** 6 m **5.** Compare the height of the window with the height of the wall. Estimate how many windows would fit on the wall. Multiply this value by 3.

Lesson 9-2

1. Find the number of kilometers light travels in one second.
2. a kilometer **3.** 299,792,458 m **4.** smaller **5.** 1,000
6. 299,732.458 **7.** 299,732 km **8.** Multiply your answer by 1,000. **9.** 44,320 ÷ 1,000 ≈ 44; 44 kg

Lesson 9-3

1. the area of a stamp **2.** $A = \ell \times w$ **3.** 0.31 in. **4.** 0.37 in.
5. $A = (0.37)(0.31)$ **6.** 0.1147 in.^{2} **7.** Divide your answer by either 0.31 or 0.37. The result should be the other number.
8. $A = 28 \times 36 = 1,008$; 1,008 in.^{2}

Lesson 9-4

1. the height of a parallelogram **2.** the area of the parallelogram and the length of the base **3.** $A = bh$
4. $66 = 5h$ **5.** division **6.** $\frac{66}{5} = 13.2$; 13.2 in. **7.** Sample answers: Multiply the answer by 5. The product is 66, so the answer checks. **8.** $A = bh$; $96 = 4b$; $b = 24$; 24 cm

Lesson 9-5

1. the circumference of each hoop **2.** Sample answer: Use the formula $C = \pi d$. **3.** 24 in.; 30 in. **4.** $24 \times 3 = 72$; 72 in.
5. $30 \times 3 = 90$; 90 in. **6.** $90 - 72 = 18$; 18 in. **7.** Inches; circumference is a length, like perimeter.
8. 30 in. − 21 in. = 9; 9 in.

Lesson 9-6

1. the area of the broadcast region **2.** $A = \pi r^2$ **3.** 45 miles
4. $A = (3.14)(45)^2$ **5.** $A = 6,358$ square miles
6. The answer is reasonable because 6,358 square miles is between the estimates of 4,800 square miles and 7,500 square miles. **7.** $A = (3.14)(5)^2 = 78.5$; the area of the search region is 78.5 square miles.

Lesson 9-7

1. A face is a plane on a prism. **2.** A vertex is a point where two or three edges intersect. **3.** An edge is a line formed by the intersection of two faces. **4.** 2 bases **5.** prism
6. trapezoid **7.** trapezoidal prism **8.** 6 faces **9.** 8 vertices
10. 12 edges **11.** It has two bases. **12.** trapezoidal pyramid; 5 faces; 5 vertices; 8 edges

Lesson 9-8

1. $SA = 2(\ell \times w) + 2(w \times h) + 2(\ell \times h)$ **2.** two **3.** $SA = 2(2\ell \times 2w) + 2(2w \times 2h) + 2(2\ell \times 2h)$ **4.** $SA = 8(\ell \times w) + 8(w \times h) + 8(\ell \times h)$ **5.** 8 **6.** The surface area is quadrupled. **7.** Think of each face separately. Double each dimension. Then, calculate the surface area. **8.** The surface area is 9 times greater.

Lesson 9-9

1. length of 20 feet; width of 8 feet; height of 7 feet; radius of 3.5 feet; length of 22 feet; volume **2.** Rectangular solid, $V = \ell \times w \times h$; cylinder, $V = \pi \times r^2 \times h$ **3.** 1,120 cubic feet
4. 846.23 cubic feet **5.** cubic units **6.** Sample answer: Round the measurements and let $\pi = 3$. Use mental math to estimate each volume. Check your answer for reasonableness.
7. 3,617.28 cubic feet

Lesson 9-10

1. the number of customers who received both the free ticket and the free popcorn **2.** Sample answer: Solve a simpler problem and look for a pattern. **3.** 3 people **4.** 9 people
5. yes **6.** 13 people **7.** Yes; 10 and 15 have 13 common multiples between 1 and 418. **8.** The least common multiple of 30 min and 45 min is 90 min or 1.5 hr; 15 hr ÷ 1.5 hr = 10 times.

Answers (continued)

Lesson 10-1

1. Starting at the fourth floor; goes down 3 floors; up 8 floors
2. Find the floor at which the elevator stops.   **3.** Draw a picture of the floors and the elevator.   **4.** the fourth floor
5. the first floor   **6.** the ninth floor   **7.** the ninth floor
8. $4 - 3 + 8 = 9$; the ninth floor   **9.** 17-yard line

Lesson 10-2

1. $-4°F$; had risen; 49 degrees   **2.** Find the temperature at 7:32 A.M.   **3.** The word *risen* tells you to add.   **4.** $-4°F$
5. $49°$ **6.** $45°F$ **7.** $45 - (-4) = 49$; $49°$ difference
8. 12, or twelve over par

Lesson 10-3

1. Determine the trail's change in elevation.   **2.** subtraction
3. 6,850 feet   **4.** 5,600 feet   **5.** $6,850 - 5,600$ **6.** 1,250 feet
7. Add your answer to 5,600 to get 6,850, the starting elevation.   **8.** Yes; she has $260 left.

Lesson 10-4

1. Write an integer to express the balloon's movement.
2. descends   **3.** negative   **4.** 235 feet   **5.** 4 minutes
6. 940 feet   **7.** -940 **8.** 4 minutes   **9.** -650 feet

Lesson 10-5

1. $30; 5 days   **2.** Find which integer represents the average decrease in stock value each day.   **3.** division   **4.** $30
5. 5 days   **6.** $6 per day   **7.** -6 **8.** -30; yes   **9.** $8,100

Lesson 10-6

1. A symmetrical figure has the same shape on both sides of a line of symmetry.   **2.** Plot the seven points on a coordinate plane.   **3.** $(1, 1)$ **4.** $(1, -1)$ **5.** $(-3, 0)$ **6.** $(-3, 0)$
7. yes   **8.** $(-1, -1)$ and $(2, -3)$

Lesson 10-7

1. $125; $20; $15; $8; $12; $35   **2.** Find how much money you have left.   **3.** $125   **4.** $90   **5.** $125 - 90$ **6.** $35   **7.** Add the amount spent to the answer for Step 6 to get $125.   **8.** $75

Lesson 10-8

1. The amount of money you make after you pay for expenses.
2. For part *a*, substitute 400 and 500 for the number of cookies sold and then simplify. For part *b*, substitute 0 for the profit and solve for the number of cookies sold.   **3.** $-$300
4. $-$225   **5.** 0   **6.** p **7.** 800 cookies   **8.** 0
9. $d = 2r$; 20 miles

Lesson 10-9

1. the instrument each person plays   **2.** Sample answer: Use logical reasoning.   **3.** violin   **4.** clarinet, trumpet, drum
5. violin, drum, trumpet; clarinet   **6.** trumpet   **7.** yes
8. Tom plays football, Troy plays tennis, Ty plays baseball, and Tia plays soccer.

Lesson 11-1

1. Find the probability of selecting a yellow balloon at random.
2. A number that describes how likely it is that an event will occur   **3.** $P = \frac{\text{number of favorable outcomes}}{\text{total number of outcomes}}$ **4.** 5 yellow balloons   **5.** 25 balloons   **6.** $\frac{5}{25}$ or $\frac{1}{5}$ **7.** $\frac{1}{5} = 0.2$ **8.** $\frac{1}{5} \times 100$ or 20%   **9.** Sample answer: Change each answer to a fraction. Each should equal $\frac{1}{5}$.   **10.** $\frac{8}{25} = 0.32 = 32\%$

Lesson 11-2

1. Find the experimental probability of the player missing a free throw.   **2.** The probability of an event based on experimental data.   **3.** $P = \frac{\text{number of times an event occurs}}{\text{total number of trials}}$
4. 12 trials   **5.** 8 misses   **6.** $\frac{8}{12}$ or $\frac{2}{3}$ **7.** He misses more. Yes, this agrees with the probability.   **8.** $\frac{4}{12} = \frac{1}{3}$

Lesson 11-3

1. the number of faulty gadgets in the day's production
2. a proportion   **3.** $\frac{7}{100}$ **4.** $\frac{n}{5,000}$ **5.** $\frac{7}{100} = \frac{n}{5,000}$; $n = 350$
6. 350 gadgets   **7.** Divide the answer by $\frac{7}{100}$ to get 5,000.
8. $\frac{4}{50} = \frac{n}{300}$; $n = 24$; 24 CDs will be faulty.

Lesson 11-4

1. The least amount of money you need to spend to get all four prizes.   **2.** $\frac{1}{4}$ **3.** 4 boxes   **4.** $13.50   **5.** not likely
6. $17

Lesson 11-5

1. the total number of possible outcomes.   **2.** Draw a tree diagram or use the counting principle.   **3.** 4   **4.** 3
5. $4 \times 3 = 12$ outcomes   **6.** 1 outcome   **7.** $\frac{1}{12}$ **8.** For each spinner number, there are 3 possible cards. Show each spinner number branching to all 3 cards.   **9.** $\frac{3}{12} = \frac{1}{4}$

Answers (continued)

Lesson 11-6

1. A permutation is an arrangement of objects in a particular order. **2.** lists, tree diagram, counting principle **3.** 4 choices **4.** 3 choices **5.** 2 choices **6.** 1 choice **7.** $4 \times 3 \times 2 \times 1 = 24$ ways **8.** Yes; by making a list or a tree diagram, you can confirm that there are 24 ways. **9.** 6 ways

Lesson 11-7

1. Both events have the same probability occurring. **2.** independent events **3.** $\frac{1}{2}$ **4.** $\frac{1}{2}$ **5.** $\frac{1}{2} \times \frac{1}{2}$ **6.** $\frac{1}{4}$ **7.** boy, boy; boy, girl; girl, boy; girl, girl; yes. **8.** $\frac{1}{2} \times \frac{1}{2} \times \frac{1}{2} = \frac{1}{8}$

Lesson 12-1

1. Commission is pay earned as a percent of sales **2.** the sales total for the week **3.** Solve the equation for s, the sales total. **4.** Subtract 250 from both sides. **5.** $0.08s = 160$ **6.** Divide both sides by 0.08. **7.** $s = 2,000$ **8.** \$2,000 **9.** Multiply by 0.08 and add \$250; \$410. **10.** $0.08s + 250 = 650$; \$5,000; The sales total was \$5,000.

Lesson 12-2

1. A mathematical statement that contains inequality symbols. **2.** No trucks over 3 tons. **3.** no **4.** yes **5.** 3 tons **6.** $w \leq 3$ tons **7.** 3 tons $\geq w$ **8.** $a \geq 18$ years

Lesson 12-3

1. the amount of money you can spend on each T-shirt **2.** $<$ **3.** $2t + 13$ **4.** $2t + 13 < 30$ **5.** Subtract 13. **6.** $2t < 17$ **7.** Divide by 2. **8.** $t < 8.5$ **9.** less than \$8.50 **10.** No, then you would spend \$30. You want to spend *less than* \$30. **11.** $2t + 13 < 40$; $2t < 27$; $t < 13.5$; you can spend less than \$13.50.

Lesson 12-4

1. the number of floors in One Atlantic Center **2.** Work backwards. **3.** 110 floors **4.** $110 + 40$ or 150 floors **5.** The John Hancock building has twice as many floors as One Atlantic Center. **6.** $2h + h = 150$ **7.** $3h = 150$; 50 floors **8.** Double the answer and add it to itself. Subtract 40. You should get 110. **9.** 10 bracelets

Lesson 12-5

1. Square the length of the side. **2.** the area of a square; the length of the side of the square **3.** 52,900 m^2 **4.** 230 m **5.** 230 m **6.** Square the answer. It should be equal to 52,900 m^2. **7.** 36 in.

Lesson 12-6

1. a right triangle **2.** the Pythagorean Theorem **4.** $9^2 + 40^2 = c^2$ **5.** $1,681 = c^2$ **6.** Take the square root of each side. **7.** 41 **8.** 41 ft **9.** Square your answer. Then see if $9^2 + 40^2$ equals that number. **10.** $18^2 + 80^2 = c^2$; $6,724 = c^2$; $82 = c$; the wire must be 82 ft.